9.50

THE TEACHING OF MATHEMATICS

Essays by A. Ya. Khinchin

Edited by B. V. Gnedenko

THE TEACHING OF
MATHEMATICS

Essays by
A. Ya. Khinchin
edited by B. V. Gnedenko

Translated from the Russian by
W. Cochrane and D. Vere-Jones

AMERICAN ELSEVIER PUBLISHING COMPANY, INC.
NEW YORK 1968

Originally Published as
   Pedogogicheski Stat'i by *A. Ya Khinchin*
Edited by B. V. Gnedenko and published by
the Academy of Pedagogical Sciences
of the RSFRS, Moscow, 1963

This edition first published by
The English Universities Press Limited 1968

American edition published by
American Elsevier Publishing Company, Inc.
52 Vanderbilt Avenue, New York, N.Y. 10017

Library of Congress Catalog Card Number: 68-15706

Printed in Great Britain

CONTENTS

INTRODUCTION

In the years since the end of the Second World War there has been a tremendous interest in this country in the problems of the content of mathematical curricula in school and university. Due to the sharing of a common language, it has been easy for American and British mathematicians to familiarise themselves with each others thoughts in these matters. It has not been so easy for them to become acquainted with thinking in the Soviet Union on matters concerning the teaching of mathematics. For that reason, mathematicians will be grateful to the translators and the publishers for making available (in English) the views of a distinguished Russian mathematician who was interested in the problems of the teaching of mathematics at all levels. The value of the translation is considerably enhanced by Dr. Vere-Jones' survey of the school system in the U.S.S.R. and the place of mathematics teaching within it.

University of Glasgow
1968   Ian N. Sneddon.

TRANSLATORS' FOREWORD

The name of the Russian mathematician A. Ya. Khinchin must be already well-known even beyond the bounds of the Soviet Union. During the last dozen years or so a number of his popular books have been translated into English (such as the 'Elementary Introduction to Probability Theory' (with B. V. Gnedenko) (118)[1], the 'Three Pearls of Number Theory' (120), and most recently 'Eight Lectures on Mathematical Analysis' (116)), to mention nothing of his fundamental contributions to number theory and the theory of probability, which have been familiar to specialists in these fields for many years. It is probably less well-known that in addition to his mathematical writing and research, Khinchin throughout his life took an active interest in the development of Soviet education, in particular, of course, of Soviet mathematical education. For many years he was a Presidium member of the Academy of Pedagogical Sciences in Moscow, and head of its section on mathematical education. His views on this subject found expression not only in his books, but more especially in a series of articles that appeared at various times in the Soviet educational press. After Khinchin's death in 1959, these articles were collected together and edited by his former pupil, Professor B. V. Gnedenko, and published in book form in 1963 under the title 'Pedagogical Essays'[2].

Our aim in the present volume has been to select and translate those of the 'Pedagogical Essays' which seemed to us to have most interest for the English reader, and to supplement them with some background material concerning Khinchin's life and the educational environment for which his articles were written.

The four articles which have been translated constitute the main part of the Russian edition, and cover a wide range of topics, from the teaching of elementary arithmetic to the character-building effects of mathematical research. Khinchin held strong, sometimes quite controversial views on the content and procedure of mathematical education. His views, however, usually strike one with their particular clarity, and are always put forward with sympathy and humour. We hope that the

[1]Numbers in brackets refer to the bibliography in the Russian edition. All of Khinchin's works referred to in the text, together with English translations where available, will be found in the lists at the end of appendix I (p. 113).

[2]'Pedagogicheskie Stat'i Izdatel'stvo Akademii Pedagogicheskikh Nauk RSFSR, Moscow, 1963.

publication of these essays will be of direct practical value to mathematics teachers, as well as providing them with some insight into the problems and circumstances of their colleagues in the Soviet Union.

In addition to the four articles translated, the Russian edition contains two further short articles by Khinchin, 'A many-sided, practical education for Soviet Youth', and 'On so-called "problems to be done in the head" in the arithmetic course'. The first of these is a hard-hitting critique of Soviet mathematical education as it was in 1939, when the article was written. It is still of considerable interest, but rather than translate in full, we have included the most important sections as part of a general survey of the development of mathematical education in the Soviet Union. This survey takes up the second of the two appendices in the present volume; it contains in addition some material on the structure of the present-day Soviet school system, and the contents of their mathematics courses. The factual material here is largely taken from the series of lectures that were given recently by Professor Gnedenko in Australia and New Zealand[1]. The second of the two untranslated articles concerns a rather special problem of Soviet arithmetic texts in the 1930's, and did not seem to us to warrant translation.

We have also included, in the first appendix, a slightly abbreviated version of the two biographical sketches which form the final section of the Russian edition. It is much to be regretted that the biographical details are so skimpy. Khinchin's life covered all the crucial events in Soviet history, and it would be fascinating to know how he reacted to the changing Soviet scene. During his youth, he was a contemporary and acquaintance of such figures as Mayakovski, but unlike Mayakovski, who committed suicide in 1930, he remained on the scene throughout Stalin's rise to power and the second World War, until the emergence of Khruschev in the 1950's. Throughout this period, he seems to have been a respected if modest figure. He was a recipient of the Stalin prize in 1941, and of the order of Lenin. How does a man of Khinchin's calibre reconcile himself to life in the Soviet Union and what were his views on its future? We can only guess at the answers from the scanty clues that remain in his works and the brief biographical details provided in the two sketches.

In conclusion, we should like to express our thanks to numerous helpers; above all, to Professor B. V. Gnedenko, who has been most helpful in the preparation of this translation, and to whom we are indebted for the tables and syllabus material which occurs in the appendix. We are also grateful to Dr T. H. Rigby and Dr R. F. D. Hutchings, who read through the appendix on Soviet education, and saved us from a number of errors, as well as providing valuable com-

[1]See, for example, the 'Australian Mathematics Teacher' **21** No. 3, November 1965, pp. 49–59.

ments and further points of information. The Australian National University provided editorial assistance, and we are especially grateful to Mrs. B. Cranston in this regard. The germ of this project was laid when one of the translators held a British Council exchange scholarship to the Soviet Union, and it is a pleasure to record our appreciation of their organization. Finally, we are indebted to the editors of 'Mathematics Teaching', and 'Science', and to the authors concerned, for permission to reproduce extracts from articles which originally appeared in these journals.

FROM THE INTRODUCTION TO THE RUSSIAN EDITION, BY B. V. GNEDENKO

The present collection of essays by the famous mathematician and teacher Alexander Yakovlevich Khinchin contains articles devoted to some questions of school mathematics teaching.

Khinchin's basic interests in teaching were not concerned with the problems of a particular method, nor the best exposition of this or that section of the course. He considered that too strict a regulation of a teacher's behaviour, the imposition of a rigid system and order of presentation, would only paralyze the teacher's initiative, depriving him of inspiration and destroying his particular individuality.

This, of course, did not mean that Khinchin denied the need for methodological studies, for seeking out the most successful ways of teaching one or other section of the secondary school course. On the contrary, he supported research of this kind, and enthusiastically encouraged the widest possible exchange of teaching skills. He did oppose, however, the methodological stereotype, that method of teaching which recognizes only one system of exposition as being valid and sees all others as erroneous and harmful. To a large extent, teaching is an art, and cannot therefore be subjected to a rigid pattern. Even quite excellent methods of teaching are, as a rule, doomed to failure if they are mechanically repeated by another teacher, without taking into account the exceedingly complex psychological features of a particular class of pupils.

At this point I should like to cite a quotation from Khinchin's foreword to Issue No. 6 of the 1946 'Information Bulletin of the RSFSR Academy of Pedagogical Sciences", devoted to mathematics teaching, where his ideas appear rather clearly. Describing the articles in the bulletin, he says,

'Each article deals with an important, even profound, theme, and by discussing it scientifically, awakens and stimulates a scientific approach in the reader's thinking. It is very pleasing that each of the articles has a discursive rather than a 'directive' character, and is written with great feeling. Excited by his own understanding of the question, the author provokes the reader to object, and in this way to work out his own particular point of view.'

Further on he emphasizes most insistently that the articles he has reviewed, having

'as their aim, an original discussion of distinct and important, but often neglected, sections of the school mathematics course, undoubtedly make a valuable contribution to the science of teaching, principally because each of them breathes a spirit of scientific alertness, and awakens the creative thought processes of the mathematics teacher.'

To awaken creative thinking, to work out the most successful ways of doing this: these, according to Khinchin, are the basic aims of teaching methodology and indeed of the whole process of teaching. For him, the success of the teaching process does not lie in the number of 'goods' and 'excellents' that the teacher gives to his class, nor the accuracy with which the teacher follows the instructions given in the teaching manuals; but in how deeply the pupils understand the ideas behind the mathematical methods used, how far they develop the ability to make accurate and full-valued logical judgements, to what extent they become apt at discerning contradictions in the logical steps of a proof, how well they learn to handle problems of non-standard type and work out proofs on their own. From this springs his impassioned fight against formalism in the teaching of mathematics and his constant appeals to lessen the gap between the requirements of life, and school training and education.

While giving due importance to particular problems of teaching methods, Khinchin constantly drew attention to the need to define and thoroughly examine the overall problems in the Soviet system of teaching mathematics. He did not tire of talking about this in his speeches, reviews of other researchers' work, and his own articles.

In the foreword already quoted he stated this point with particular force:

'Only in one respect does the scientific output of the Department deserve some reproach; it is obvious that, with such a highly qualified staff, the Department could undertake work on more responsible themes. The basic foundations of mathematics teaching in Soviet schools, a thorough scientific examination of their syllabuses, research into the general requirements of mathematics text-books—this is the type of theme one would like to see in the scientific accoutrements of the Department. It stands to reason that these themes could not be undertaken by one man alone, no matter how highly qualified he might be. Such work would require collective effort.'

Khinchin set two requirements for teaching mathematics in the schools:

1. Factors such as the students' ages may make necessary a simplified presentation of scientific ideas and concepts. However, this simplification must in no circumstances lead to a contradiction with the scientific treatment of the question.

2. The substitution, for exact definitions and principles, of vague statements containing no precise meaning can never facilitate an understanding of the subject. Khinchin said that thinking in foggy terms can never be easier than thinking in precise terms.

He carefully observed these principles in his practical work. For example, these ideas exerted a considerable influence on his well-known re-edition of A. P. Kiselev's text-book of arithmetic. As a result, a whole series of concepts, retained in teaching practice only through blind tradition, were deleted from the text-book. The book was immediately successful in two respects: it was more scientific, and it was easier to understand. Small wonder that Kiselev himself wrote to A. Ya Khinchin, expressing his sincere gratitude for the work carried out on his book.

Closely related to this re-edition of Kiselev's text-book is a small article 'On the concept of the ratio of two numbers'. Time has convincingly shown how right Khinchin was to protest against the way this concept was then understood. It was completely alien to modern mathematics, and is now remembered by scarcely anyone. Nevertheless, it called for great courage to stand up for this point of view.

To the extent that this article has retained only an historical interest, we have not included it in the present collection. We may, however, cite here a short quotation from it, which characterizes an important aspect of the author's teaching principles.

'Our wish—as far as possible to endow the school treatment of a subject with its full meaning in present-day science—is clear, and can stand without need of further justification. Objections to it should not be based on obsolete traditions. As it is, we have oriented our school mathematics courses for too long on outdated models, ignoring the entire progress of science. This is a completely intolerable situation, which has long since been done away with in other subjects (physics, chemistry, biology). The only problem which sometimes prevents giving a scientific treatment of a concept in the school course is the difficulty of this treatment, which may make it necessary to seek ways of simplifying it. On those occasions (which occur only too frequently in mathematics) when the scientific treatment of the concept is simpler and clearer than the traditional treatment, there can be no justification whatsoever for retaining the latter.

'Reference to tradition would, and with good reason, protect the "yat" and "fita"[1]; our orthography, however, made short work of them a long time ago. It is a cause of wonder sometimes at just how many of these "yats" are still preserved in school mathematics, and what desperate resistance is stirred up in the fight against them.'

These words are timely even now. Indeed, what a great amount of traditional material is still preserved in the secondary school course, and how tightly the defenders of the old school cling to it! How much

[1]Fita and yat—letters of the old Russian alphabet surviving in the language only by tradition and pronounced exactly as the other letters eff and yeh. Reference to them here is used in the sense of implying the need for a systematic war on unnecessary, outdated concepts that only make our life more complicated. B.V.G.

hopelessly outdated material is still taught, closing the way to what is new and extremely necessary, and hindering the pupils from obtaining a correct view of mathematics and the reasons for its ever-increasing influence on literally all fields of human activity. Moreover, such traditions bar mathematics teachers from applying contemporary mathematical methods (which are often, in point of fact, quite elementary) to the study of the phenomena of life around them. They make it impossible for many talented representatives of our teaching profession to turn their abilities to the contemporary problems of mathematics and its teaching methods.

The articles included in the present collection were written by A. Ya. Khinchin at various periods of his career, and, naturally, their contents reflect the vital problems raised from time to time by Soviet society concerning school education. But these problems have not lost their topicality even now. In fact, the questions posed by Khinchin are not likely to lose their educational acuity, for they were chosen with a profound understanding of the basic difficulties encountered in mathematics teaching, and the traditions building up in our teaching circles.

New questions have appeared, of course, especially following the Soviet government's recent decrees aimed at drawing school education closer to the requirements of life. Instead of exercising a weakening effect, however, these changes have served to emphasize still further the importance of the problems with which Khinchin was concerned. How topical even now is his appeal for a total and unremitting fight against formalism in the teaching of mathematics! For the work of bringing the classroom closer to life does not mean mechanically learning by heart the syllabus material; but, in the first place, clearly presenting the subject's basic concepts and results, and then establishing liaisons between the subject-matter of the sciences and practical problems. This is particularly important at the present time, when mathematical methods are assuming a more and more fundamental place, not only in the realm of scientific work, but also in immediate economic and technical applications. The nation is continually raising its demands on workers in all fields to analyze logically, using mathematical tools, the phenomena of nature, and many economic, technical and other processes.

We include in the present collection two works[1] prepared for the press a long time ago by Alexander Yakovlevich, but for some reason not submitted by him for publication. Possibly the author saw some deficiencies in their literary style, or considered that he had not completely elaborated his ideas in them. It is hard now to say why they were held back.

The manuscript of the article 'On the educative effects of mathematics lessons' was handed to me by N. A. Khinchina, the late teacher's widow.

[1] Only the first of these is included in the translation.

I discovered the second work, 'On the so-called "Problems to be done in the head"' among A. Ya. Khinchin's papers. The workers of the mathematics section of the Institute of General and Polytechnic Education of the RSFSR Academy of Pedagogical Sciences told me that the author himself brought these manuscripts to the notice of the teaching community. In particular, the paper 'On the educative effects of mathematics lessons' was read by A. Ya. Khinchin at one of the scientific meetings of the department. There is no doubt that the publication of both manuscripts will be of benefit to our mathematics teachers.

In the first of the above manuscripts Khinchin referred twice to a proposed work in which he was intending to deal mainly with the question of teaching the elements of mathematical analysis in secondary schools. The study of these questions would be very timely today, and it can only be regretted that no trace remains of Khinchin's ideas on these subjects, as he was one of the most outstanding of our university lecturers, and for many years delivered courses on mathematical analysis in universities and teaching institutes.

His audiences considered these lectures to be the best they attended during their student years. This is hardly surprising, because Khinchin strove to convey to his audience not merely the formal apparatus, not merely a sequence of transformations, but above all the 'soul' of the subject, its underlying ideas. And this he achieved brilliantly! His excellent 'A Short Course of Mathematical Analysis' (144) soon ran into several editions in Russian, and has been translated into many European and Asian languages. Nevertheless it conveys only to a small degree the charm of Khinchin's own lively, picturesque, literary, and logically perfect lectures.

His ideas on teaching the fundamentals of analysis are obviously present in embryonic form in his 'Eight Lectures on Mathematical Analysis' (116). In many respects this book may be regarded as a model of educational tact and beautiful mathematical expression. Severity and clarity, a sparing use of words, and, at the same time, a highly artistic form of presentation, characterize all of Khinchin's works, both large and small. In some ways, the traits of his style are concentrated very clearly in the 'Eight lectures'.

Because of his outstanding qualities as a teacher in the Soviet higher schools, we have included in this collection, in addition to his own articles on secondary schools, two articles written about Khinchin himself.

We did not think it possible to include in the present collection two small articles, 'The introduction of irrational numbers' (97), and 'Complex numbers' (98), because neither work deals with its subject fully.

Two other manuscripts deserve mention. In the archives of the Institute of General and Polytechnic Education, formerly known as the Institute of Teaching Methods, there is a short report by Khinchin entitled 'Elements of teaching probability in schools'. In those years Khinchin considered it advisable to introduce the elements of probability theory into the secondary school mathematics course for these reasons:

1. A knowledge of probability theory would provide a good preparation for the many pupils who, in one way or another, are required to deal with the analysis of statistical data in the professions they enter on leaving school.

2. Problems involving the calculations of probabilities offer a concrete application of combinatorial formulae, and would help the pupils to acquire a firmer and more conscious understanding of these formulae.

I am convinced that the idea of including the basic elements of probability theory in the school mathematics course is worth a thorough examination. Statistical methods have, in fact, widely penetrated scientific and technical practices in our lifetime, and many school pupils will have to deal with them, including those who enter industry. In some countries—Japan, Yugoslavia, and to some extent the U.S.A. —the foundations of probability theory are already taught in the schools. In the experimental text book on probability written by a group of American authors (Douglas, Mosteller-Wilkes and others), connections between the methods of probability theory and everyday life are revealed in almost every chapter. Their statements at the beginning of Chapter 7 are particularly interesting: during the second World War the U.S.A. administration on War Industry, in the years 1942–45 only, arranged thirty-three short-term courses for persons in a position to carry out statistical control of production quality. By 1957, the application of statistical methods of quality control saved American industry an estimated four billion dollars for this one year alone.

By now it has become possible and even necessary to speak of the need for introducing the elements of probability theory and mathematical statistics from other standpoints than just that of mathematical education. We have to bear in mind the important re-thinking of all our ideas which is associated with the introduction of the concept of 'randomness'. This concept now penetrates all aspects of our life—science, economics, social life, medicine, teaching. It is not possible to withhold from the rising generation one of the central concepts of our age. The concept must be introduced gradually, making use not only of mathematics lessons, but also of lessons in physics, biology, and social studies.

Finally, in those of Khinchin's papers which have been kept, there are fragmentary notes on the character of teaching, comments on the manuscripts of works brought to him, and brief remarks on lectures he had heard and articles he had read. These notes deserve a searching analysis. I should like to quote here a small extract from notes he made on three block pads, relating to his appraisal of some large manuscript (there are references to pages 69–70 of the text).

'Types of revision:
  1. Revision at the beginning of studies
  2. Revision at the beginning of the school year
  3. Current revision during the lesson
  4. Revision for tests
  5. Annual revision
  6. Revision in preparation for the examinations.
  What a nightmare! Isn't there some way of teaching, so that, instead of these endless repetitions, the material would not be forgotten?"

These words pose what is undoubtedly a very important question— how must one teach, so that the thing taught is firmly embedded in the memory, and embedded not as ballast, but as a tool ready for action? A surfeit of repetition is not necessarily the best way out of this situation.

The attentive reader familiar with the works of A. Ya. Khinchin may reproach us for some narrow-mindedness over the selection of articles for the present collection. It is true that even some of the more specialized works of A. Ya. Khinchin may be of undoubted interest to the teacher from several points of view. Among such works, I would like to draw attention in particular to those which appear in our list under the numbers (34), (43), (80), (131), (140), (141), (152)[1]. In them he is concerned with questions which, on the one hand, could serve as subjects for a school mathematics discussion group, and, on the other, are useful to obtain a general philosophical view of the concepts and ideas of mathematics.

It would be appropriate to include also in a collection of Khinchin's educational works separate paragraphs and chapters from his books (73), (116), (113), (118), (120), (140)[1], which brilliantly portray his mastery as an author and teacher, and which at the same time would be of value to the secondary school teacher. To do so, however, would be to break the unity of purpose in the present collection.

In the concluding section of the book we present a biographical sketch, in which we indicate those directions of scientific research where Khinchin made a substantial contribution. The fact that the regions of contemporary mathematics touched on in this sketch are still far from the school mathematics course is particularly instructive;

[1]These works are listed by their number in the bibliography at the end of appendix I.

Khinchin's life demonstrates clearly that scientific research of a mathematical character does not oppose but, on the contrary, admirably complements the work of a teacher. A list of Khinchin's scientific works is attached to the biographical note. References in the text to Khinchin's works are given in brackets, indicating the number of the article on the list.

I should like to take this opportunity to express my gratitude to all those who have helped to prepare the present collection by their individual comments and by supplying references to details of A. Ya. Khinchin's scientific, educational, and social activities with which I was not familiar.

Professor Gnedenko has added the following note for the English edition:
Khinchin's articles on education were written in the period 1938–49. Since that time there have been many changes in the countries of the Soviet Union, and in Soviet schools. A thorough experiment has been carried out on introducing into school education the elements of training in production work, including the direct participation of all physically sound school children as workers in factories. In the mathematics course, the intervening years have seen the introduction of the elements of mathematical analysis and vector algebra, alterations in the structure of algebra and trigonometry courses—now transformed into the elements of the theory of elementary functions—and the adoption of the notion of geometrical transformation as one of the fundamental ideas in teaching geometry.

At the present time ever more insistent voices are being raised with demands for the necessity of a more thorough-going transformation of the school mathematics course. In our country two commissions have been set up, one from the Presidium of the Academy of Sciences of the USSR, and the other from the Presidium of the Academy of Pedagogical Sciences; both are chaired by Academician A. N. Kolmogorov.

BASIC CONCEPTS OF MATHEMATICS IN THE SECONDARY SCHOOLS[1]

Section 1: The Concept of Number

The level of ideas in the mathematics taught at secondary schools lags well behind the development of modern mathematics. In no other school discipline are we confronted with a state of affairs where, with only the odd exception, all the material covered is made up of facts which were already well-known in the seventeenth century. Only one chapter of the algebra course—the study of irrational numbers—belongs among the inventions of the nineteenth century.

A partial explanation of the outdated character of the syllabus material can be found in the fact that in mathematics (as distinct from physics, chemistry, and biology) the higher institutes at once take their students to a higher level and never return to the elementary notions. However, it is quite impossible to explain or justify the widely accepted fact that, as a result of centuries-old tradition, even the most basic concepts, formulations and methods of arguments are expounded in the schools in a manner which has no relation to their treatment and understanding in contemporary mathematical science. Any reference to the obvious help in understanding the relevant concept achieved by these means is quite unfounded; in the overwhelming majority of cases the scientific picture of the relevant concept is the more simple and straightforward, and in every case it is more precise than that fostered by tradition in the text-books. Almost always, such a reference has the aim of masking a stale or routine methodological approach; often the whole attempt to justify it reduces to no more than a statement that 'the old ways are better'. But in no case have I been able to discover why the old ways should be better, and in all cases I have come to the conclusion that it would be better only for the teacher who has learnt off the text-book by heart and does not wish to have to start re-learning, and by no means better for the pupils; that in all cases it was an attempt by a teacher in the backward set of his profession to justify his position, whereas leading teachers became interested in the new ideas, thought them over keenly, and often accepted them.

I would like to set down two principles as a basis for answering the

[1]First published in 'Matematika v shkole', 1939, under the title 'Osnovnie ponyatiya matematiki v srednei shkole'.

question of to what extent—bearing in mind the development of the schoolchild himself—this or that concept can be studied in the school course in a manner which accords with its treatment in contemporary mathematical science; here are these principles:

1. In those cases where the age level does not permit such a treatment of the subject as would be accepted by contemporary mathematics, a simplified picture can be given in the school course; this means that the school is not bound to take the development of each concept up to its level in contemporary mathematics, but can stop at an earlier stage. But in no case must the schools *falsify* the scientific treatment of the concept in the aims of simplifying it, or give it features which contradict the way it is understood in mathematical science—features which later have to be rooted out. In other words, in no case should the school develop the concept in a direction which bears away from the direction of its treatment in mathematical science.

2. The replacement of sharp, exact definitions, formulations and arguments by foggy ones having no precise meaning, and in further use leading inevitably to logical difficulties, can in no circumstances ease the burden of understanding, but on the contrary will always make it more difficult; to think in foggy terms cannot be easier than to think in precise terms.

Finally, we would suggest that in its usual form the school course is filled with concepts which are either unknown to mathematical science, or were long ago rejected by it. In the great majority of cases, the retention of such concepts, deliberately thought up for the schools and unknown to science, has nothing to speak for it save blind tradition; there is no methodological justification for burdening the course with such concepts, and it can only do harm.

These are the basic principles on which this book—perhaps somewhat unusual in its content—is written; the reader will find in it neither a more or less popular account of modern scientific ideas, intended to improve his qualifications, nor a dissertation on methodology in the customary sense of the word. Yet I would like to express the hope that in reading it the teacher will encounter both ideas that will broaden his scientific outlook, and some methodological assistance. The modest aim of the book is to take some basic mathematical concepts and to work over the question of to what extent and by what means their study in the secondary schools can be brought into correspondence with their treatment in contemporary mathematics.

The Concept of Number in the Secondary School

The concept of number is the hub of the whole school course in mathematics, entering into it from the first class to the last. Thus the historical evolution of this concept in the pupil's mind takes place over a long period: over such a period, indeed, that in its course the growth of the pupil's mind can be compared with the growth of the mind of mankind over the whole history of man's conscious life. And as the concept of number has grown from step to step in the consciousness of thinking man, assuming at different epochs forms that are different not only in content but also in style—so in exactly the same way we should not speak of a single concept of number corresponding to the state of consciousness of a schoolchild. During the course of school study, the concept of number is not only enriched in content, so as to include ever wider and wider classes of numbers, but also evolves qualitatively together with the child's understanding, acquiring new features and shades of meaning, and continually rising to higher and higher levels of abstraction and logical perfection. Even the motivation of successive extensions to the idea of number takes on different forms at different stages of growth, just as in the history of science these same extensions, having as their general cause the demands of man's practical experience, in fact won their claims to existence by calling on quite different problems and aspects of man's understanding. If we can motivate the introduction of fractions by calling directly on practical considerations, and we could hardly hope to achieve better results by appealing to considerations of a more theoretical character, then in introducing negative numbers we can already count on the significant pedagogical effects of the remark that in the new domain it is always possible to form the difference of two numbers. In introducing irrational numbers, besides analogous arguments, we can refer with good effect to the theoretical needs of geometry. Finally, the introduction of complex numbers is tackled at an age when the pupil with average development should already be in a position to appreciate the considerable theoretical implications of this last extension to the concept of number. Not only the stage, the degree of evolution itself, but also the *level of understanding* of this evolutionary process is different at different stages of education. And of course, only in the final class will it be in order to take a full, retrospective glance at the overall picture of the completed evolutionary process.

The concept of number is distinguished from many other concepts of the school course by its *primarity*. This means that in the overwhelming majority of ways in which mathematics can be developed as a logical system, the idea of number belongs to the set of those concepts which are not defined in terms of other concepts, but together with the axioms enter into the ranks of the initial data. It means that mathematics does not contain within itself an answer to the question 'what is a number?' —an answer, that is, which would consist of a definition of this concept in terms of concepts that had been introduced at an earlier stage; mathematics gives this answer in a different form, by listing the properties of a number as axioms. It would, of course, be even more senseless and futile to attempt to define this concept in the school courses of arithmetic and algebra; and in particular we should beware of the rather widespread tendency to create substitutes for such definitions by passing off as a definition of the concept a list of those places in man's practical experience where the concept is useful. It is obviously necessary that the schoolchild should know how and why the requirements of calculation and measurement led to the rise and consequent extension of the concept of number; but to set children to learn by heart such phrases as 'a number is the result of a calculation or a measurement', or 'a ratio is the result of a comparison', etc., and to suppose that such phrases constitute an answer to the questions 'what is a number?' and 'what is a ratio?' (that is provide *definitions* of those concepts) amounts to accustoming the pupils deliberately to logical vagueness and inaccuracy, to confusing logical definitions with generic descriptions. From such a 'definition' the pupils will learn as much of number as the man who has never heard the word 'war' would learn of it from the phrase 'war is the result of the collision of national interests.'

We believe it is important to insist that the whole school course should be freed from any attempt to give a direct answer to the question 'what is a number?', because no matter what the answer might be, it could only amount to a vulgarization, falsifying the logical content of the problem. Of course, we shall be asked, what then should one say, as a teacher, if the pupil asks this question? Our answer: act as ever—that is, tell him the truth; tell him that the question he has posed is one of the most difficult questions in the philosophy of science, one to which we are still far from having a complete answer; that a number, in the same way as any mathematical concept, is the reflection in our own consciousness of certain relations in the real world; but that the question, precisely which relations of the real world find their reflection in the concept of number, which relations are *quantitative*, is a deep and difficult philosophical problem; mathematics itself can only point out to those who study it what types of numbers there are, what are their properties, and how they can and should be manipulated. If such an answer does not satisfy the pupil, it signifies only that that particular pupil has not yet reached the stage where he can have a proper understanding of the problems involved in the question he has asked; with this the teacher must be content; it is better to wait with the answer for another year, than to substitute for that answer a surrogate which vulgarizes the problem.

But if, in the school mathematics course, we elect not to give a logical definition of the concept of number, this by no means implies that we can leave to themselves the formation and evolution of those ideas and associations which the pupil makes with the word 'number'.

On the contrary, right throughout the pupil's period of study, the teacher must lead him with a firm hand towards the development of a picture of number that is correct, clear-cut, and as far as possible scientifically mature, underlining everything that helps to form such a picture, and pointing out everything that may distort or falsify it.

What, then, is this correct picture of number? at what level of scientific maturity is it within the pupil's grasp to form such a picture? and by what means can the creation of such a picture be achieved?

We consider that the whole of the arithmetic and algebra course should be oriented towards gradually building up and strengthening in the pupil's mind the idea that a number is an *object of arithmetical operations*. It should be clear that not only is this phrase (or some equivalent) incapable of serving as a definition of the concept of number, but that in general it should not even be pronounced during the school course. But if by means of apt emphases and indirect remarks on the part of the teacher, the pupils at the end of the tenth class have come of themselves—perhaps only subconsciously—to associate with the word 'number' something that can be added, multiplied, etc., then we can confidently assert that as regards the concept of number the school has discharged its duties as well and at as high a level as it ever can. In this way, a platform on which to base further mathematical development, if such be needed, will be prepared in the best possible manner; for just such a concept of number is, on the one hand, undoubtedly within a schoolchild's grasp in his final year, and, on the other, a key that will open all doors into the realms of modern algebra.

The thesis we have put forward must not, of course, be understood as having in any way the nature of a call for a break with the *real* associations of the concept of number. It should go without saying that the final picture of number that we have espoused does not exclude, but necessarily includes, the idea of number as a reflection of real relations and dependences. All teaching of arithmetic and algebra in the schools should be carried on, as we shall describe below, under the banner of a fight against formalism, taking full account of the real content of each new species of number and of each new algebraical operation. If the operations of arithmetic and algebra are themselves not allowed to lose their real content in the pupils' understanding, then it will follow that the idea of number as the object of these operations, being the mature fruit of the degree of abstraction and generality that we have achieved, must not and cannot become separated from the real source of the abstracted concept; on the contrary, the operational side of the idea of number should help to underline, recall and strengthen in the pupils' minds the connections and applications of this idea.

In the account that follows we shall touch in order on some different stages in the growth of the concept of number; in doing so, our whole attention will be concentrated on the logical nature of each new extension; methodological corollaries will be considered only insofar as they are concerned with the realization of this logical nature in the teaching process. Thus nothing in what follows can pretend to the role of a methodological discussion, any more than the present article itself can make any claims to be considered a methodological handbook.

Zero

The first extension of the concept of number that the pupil meets occurs at the moment when zero is added to the natural numbers. In our methodological literature, discussion continues to the present time as to whether zero should be treated in the schools as a number, or whether it should be left as a symbol pointing to the absence of any units of the relevant type in the given number. We suggest that the latter proposition can only be the fruit of illogical thinking; there are no grounds whatsoever for taking up in the schools a position which is in contradiction to the scientific approach to arithmetic; in practice, such a position would be clearly intolerable, leading to conclusions and consequences which in the final instance would amount to the complete impossibility of any systematic building up of the study of number. Indeed,

1. The whole of modern science considers zero a number.

2. If we do not consider zero a number, then we are forced to admit that the difference (and after the introduction of negative numbers also the sum) of two numbers may not be a number.

3. If we do not consider zero a number, we are forced to perform algebraic operations (addition, subtraction, multiplication) on something that is not a number. On the other hand, by accepting zero as a number, we have, at an early stage in the educational process, the possibility of planting in the pupils' minds that operational principle of which we have already spoken (roughly according to the scheme: 'zero can be added and subtracted; it is possible to multiply by zero; hence, zero is a number').

4. Finally, the step, so frightening to many methodologists, of incorporating into the ranks of the number system a symbol which up to now has denoted precisely the *absence* of any units of the relevant type, is in fact not only free from any unscientific bias, but quite on the contrary offers us a first and very important example of the realization within mathematics of the dialectical law of the unity of opposites. When, later, we teach the pupils to understand a whole number as a particular instance of a complex number, a constant as a particular instance of a variable, etc., all of this is a manifestation of one and the same law of dialectical logic; a manifestation which is most char-

acteristic of the whole style of mathematical science:—a concept that arises initially as the antithesis of some given concept, at first standing to it in a relation of clearly expressed antagonism, later, when considered at a higher level, is synthesized with the other into a single common whole, both concepts fully retaining within this unity their opposing properties. And thus zero, while initially defined as an antithesis, as opposite in relation to the whole numbers, at a later stage in the development of the concept of number, without thereby losing its real significance or any of its particular peculiarities, moves up to stand in one line with the natural numbers, taking its place as the result of operations on numbers, obeying the same laws and rules as they do, and by the same token being itself admitted to the number world.

That is how the matter stands in principle. The image built up in the pupils' minds must, naturally, have a considerably simplified form; but simplification should entail neither distortion nor vulgarization. After zero is firmly lodged in the child's mind as a symbol representing the absence in the given number of any units of the appropriate sort, and in this way has become a familiar tool of written enumeration, he will find while mastering operations on many-figure numbers, in the actual practice of arithmetical manipulations, that willy-nilly, step by step, he is becoming accustomed to the idea that zero may also be obtained as the result of operations carried out on natural numbers, and can even be considered as the object of these operations. Then, at the proper moment, the teacher says: since we operate on zero just as simply and successfully as we do on numbers, and since it obeys all the rules of such operations just as the numbers do, we shall agree from now on to consider it as a number itself; and this agreement shall never be broken.

The addition of zero to the number world on the strength of its being the object of arithmetical operations, is the first step in bringing home to the schoolchild that operational principle of which we spoke in the introduction to this article.

Fractions

The practical motivation for bringing in fractional numbers is so convincing and so readily appreciable by a schoolchild that there is no need to give any explanations here.

From the logical point of view, several points should be emphasized. (1) Whole numbers, although initially opposed to fractions, later appear as a different species, a particular case of the latter. Here we have a second example of the realization of the law of the unity of opposites in arithmetic, and some attention should be given to this point. While, of course, saying nothing to the children of such dialectical laws, the teacher must take care that the picture of a larger world of numbers, where the long familiar whole numbers have a special place (but are not outside this world) is firmly lodged in his pupils' minds.

(2) The impossibility of dividing by zero is a consequence of the special nature of that number, which it retains after its annexation to the number world. Since this prohibition is universal (i.e. retains its strength in all further extensions of the concept of number) it must be stated and constantly called to mind in the most categorical form. Throughout the whole school course, it is essential scrupulously to avoid any notations which contain zero in the denominator. Thus, in asserting that the equation $0.x = 1$ has no solutions, the conclusion should be motivated by the consideration that for all x, $0.x$ is equal to zero, and consequently can never equal unity. Conversely, it would be improper to argue as follows, 'From $0.x = 1$, it would follow that $x = 1/0$, but since $1/0$ has no meaning, the given equation has no solution'. In such a discussion we in fact carry out a division by zero, only afterwards asserting that the expression obtained has no meaning; yet our problem was precisely to teach the pupils not to attempt to divide by zero. And this is to say nothing of such notations as $1/0 = \infty$, etc., which are quite widely accepted in our schools. They are essentially misleading, causing countless errors and bad habits, and they should therefore be driven relentlessly out of school practice.

(3) We consider it necessary to make a few remarks on the question of the role and place of decimal fraction and percentage sums in the arithmetic course. Experience shows that in this respect the simplest facts often remain unrecognized even by the teacher, and this circumstance in its turn affects the whole style of teaching and those general viewpoints by whose light the text-book material is presented to the schoolchildren.

The source of the confusion lies in the terms 'decimal fractions' and 'percentages' themselves, which create the impression that here we are concerned with some new type of fraction. In fact, of course, just those same fractions are in view which the pupils have already mastered in detail, and the only question that arises concerns a new apparatus for depicting the same old numbers, a new way of writing fractions. It would be much better, and would help significantly in reaching a proper understanding of the question, if the relevant chapters bore the titles 'Decimal notation for fractions', and 'Percentage notation for fractions', since 0.2 differs from $1/5$, $0.\dot{3}$ from $1/3$, 45% from $9/20$ in no way whatever, apart from the form of the notation; and the sooner and more firmly this is grasped by the pupils, the more easily they will tackle the difficulties associated with decimal and percentage sums. It is our strong belief that a considerable proportion of these difficulties arise from the attempts of text-book writers, methodologists and teachers to create some sort of 'difference in kind' between the expressions 0.6 and 60%

—a difference of which science knows nothing (simply identifying the meaning of all these expressions) and which is thought up especially for school needs. We stand firmly for kicking out all such parasitical pseudo-scientific baggage from the school course, having a strong conviction that such specially thought-up contrivances, incapable of being given a clear logical content, can never make understanding the relevant concepts any easier, but, on the contrary, will always make a proper understanding more difficult. One further, analogous contrivance should be mentioned in this context: instead of simply defining the ratio of two numbers as their quotient, children are set to learn by heart a 'definition', according to which 'a ratio is the result of a comparison'—a phrase to which nobody could give a precise meaning.

The situation is particularly bad in the case of percentages. Instead of pointing out from the very beginning and with the utmost clarity that percentages are nothing more than a special notation for fractions, and that consequently there are not and never could be any special 'problems on percentages', but, on the contrary any problem with the data in fractions can be formulated and solved in terms of percentages and vice versa—in place of this reasonably clear approach to the matter our schools create some sort of 'cult of percentages', referring to them as if they had some special content, and creating for them a special theory and a special category of problems; in a word, doing all that they can to ensure that a strange and difficult new concept grows up in the schoolchild's mind—the percentage—requiring a special approach and special methods of investigation. And as a rule, after all this, it is stated that 'percentages are not well mastered by the children'.

It seems to us necessary to make one more remark concerning percentages. The children may be troubled by the question, why is it necessary to have yet another form of notation for fractional numbers, when two of these—ordinary fractions and decimals—are already in existence? The older arithmetic courses answered this question simply by remarking that this form of notation was often used in commerce. To say nothing of the fact that even in those days such an answer would explain nothing, it is clear that now, in Soviet everyday life, percentage calculations have attained to such widespread usage that this answer is quite outdated. And in passing, our teacher himself is frequently hard put to it to answer this question with reasonable clarity. It may therefore be useful to devote a few words to it.

If we wish to compare two fractions quickly, at a glance, for example 8/23 and 12/35, we are hindered by the fact that these fractions are written in different parts (they have different denominators). As far as possible therefore, it is convenient for simple practical purposes to use fractional numbers (even if they are only approximate) expressed in terms of the same parts, i.e. in the form of fractions with the same denominator. What then is the most convenient number to choose for this universal denominator? The requirements of decimal notation and of the metric system of measures clearly suggest taking for such a number either 10, 100, 1000 etc. The further choice is determined on the basis of purely practical considerations. If the universal denominator is taken too small, then it may happen that by using whole numbers in the numerator we shall get too great a rounding off, and there will be insufficient accuracy for most practical purposes. On the other hand, if the universal denominator is taken extremely large, then we shall achieve good accuracy of approximation, but at the same time the numerators will also be very large numbers and therefore inconvenient for practical computation. As experience has shown, it is just the choice of the number 100 as the universal denominator which best meets all the requirements of elementary calculations: in this case adequate accuracy for the majority of practical purposes can be obtained by using whole numbers in the numerator; and as a rule the numerators are reasonably small numbers which can be operated upon without difficulty.

But the choice of 100 as the universal denominator amounts precisely to adapting the percentage notation for fractional numbers. Of course, it may still happen that in some cases the required accuracy cannot be attained by the use of whole number numerators; sometimes, therefore, we add one or even more decimal places after the decimal point (86·3 %), which in fact represents a changeover from percentages to permillia, etc.

Negative Numbers. Rational Numbers

From a practical point of view, the introduction of negative numbers arises from the requirements of measuring quantities whose values extend in two opposite directions. We meet with quantities of this type in our everyday experience; hence the practical motivation for negative numbers presents no difficulties on the methodological side. Matters are considerably more difficult when it comes to the justification of operations on negative numbers. All the difficulties connected with this section, which are well-known to the methodologist, have their root in the fact that the logical situation arising here is new and unfamiliar to the mind of the child. The discussion concerns the definition of operations carrying the usual names (addition, multiplication) on objects that are new, that have only just been introduced, and the fact that this or that operation, although carrying the familiar name, can be defined quite arbitrarily from the formal point of view, is such a new consideration that it will be taken into the child's consciousness only with great difficulty. The pupil cannot free himself from the insistent demand for a proof of the rule of signs in multiplication; yet the teacher is not only unable to give him such a proof, but quite on the contrary, from the scientific point of view he should attempt to convince the pupil that no such proof can exist, and ought not to be sought for or demanded. Our general methodological approach here gives us the correct way out of this situation, which is to take a series of examples connected with this or that concrete manifestation of negative numbers, and on their basis to attempt to convince the pupil of the reasonableness of the accepted algebraic rules. In this respect, however, there is one real danger, which must be guarded against with all due precaution. In putting forward such examples, the teacher, text-book, methodologist, must always accompany them with a clear statement that here there is no question of a proof of this or that rule, but only an illustration of its usefulness, and give some reference to the reasons why in general such a rule cannot be proved. And similarly at a later stage—while showing the pupils that under the rules set up for manipulating negative numbers, all those laws remain valid which hold for positive numbers—it is essential that the teacher should point out that here too this circumstance cannot serve as a *proof* of the definitions set up, and is only a demonstration of their *logical* reasonableness, just as earlier we had an illustration of their *practical* reasonableness. Without all these reassurances, the children will not only search unceasingly for an adequate logical basis for the rules of operating on negative numbers, but at a later stage in the course will acquire the tendency to make fruitless efforts to seek proofs of assertions which in fact are definitions of new concepts, and therefore cannot be proved (the length of the circumference of a circle is equal to the limit of the perimeters of inscribed polygons as the lengths of their sides become infinitely small, etc.).

In many authors' texts, the treatment of negative numbers contains one important feature which places it in opposition to the understanding of this concept as it is generally accepted in science; a well-known example occurs in the standard text-book and in the syllabus of the algebra course. Where, from the point of view of mathematics, the negative numbers are introduced by adding to the numbers already known (called positive numbers; zero occupies a special position) a new class of numbers called negative numbers, in almost all school expositions of the subject there is a more or less open tendency to move towards a quite different picture which has nothing in common with the scientific treatment. In its completed form, this picture would appear something as follows: to the already familiar ('absolute', unsigned) numbers is added a new class of 'relative' numbers, divided into positive numbers and negative numbers; from this point of view, a positive number as considered in algebra is in some way distinct from the absolute, unsigned number considered in arithmetic; it is supposed that $|5|$ is in some way different from $+5$, that $|5|$ is an absolute number, unsigned, whereas $+5$ is a relative number, a positive number.

This tendency is very widespread, but while certain authors state it quite clearly and unequivocally, and subsequently attempt to follow it up, with others its presence and influence can be felt only between the lines and it is only brought out clearly in incidental remarks; in very few cases do we find a clear and explicitly stated point of view which accords with the scientific treatment of the problem.

As in all similar situations, we would suggest that here too over-burdening the subject with objects and concepts unknown to science, invented especially for the needs of school-teaching, and necessarily placing that teaching in opposition to the scientific standpoint, not only fails to make the subject more easily comprehensible, but quite to the contrary obscures its logical structure without any methodological advantage, leading to confusion and logical contradictions. Why not define an absolute quantity as it is defined by mathematicians? Why introduce 'innuendoes' of use to nobody, creating ephemeral differences, needed neither in theory nor in practice, between the quantities 5, $+5$, $|+5|$, $|-5|$, all of which are exactly identical from the scientific point of view? For you see, the pupil is not told that 5 means $+5$, that the plus sign in front of a number can be omitted; why is it that in such circumstances people should wish to create the impression that in addition to the positive number five there exists some further sort of absolute number five, denoted by the same symbol 5, giving the same answer as the positive number five in all operations, and yet in some way, in some nuance, different from it? And is it really possible to think that all this rigmarole, which not even a mathematical scholar could pick his way through, is capable of making it easier for a school-child to understand negative numbers?[1]

It must be admitted that to a considerable extent the persistence of of these unscientific traditions can be blamed on the term 'relative numbers', which has no use in science, but is to the present day encountered in our text-books and syllabuses. It is in the nature of every 'relative' quantity to demand an absolute by way of correlative; as soon as a relative number makes its appearance we naturally seek for the absolute numbers. Incidentally, if a suitable name is required for the collection of both positive and negative whole and fractional numbers, including zero, then science has long had one ready to hand: rational numbers. We can only recommend that it be used in school; its derivation can easily be explained to children—a ratio is a quotient, a rational number any number that can be expressed as a quotient of two whole numbers (the often expressed objection that the pupil will immediately ask, 'But what other, irrational numbers are there?', we

---

[1] A. Ya. Khinchin's remarks on absolute numbers have now lost a lot of their force, insofar as the concept of absolute number is now introduced in the text-books in a more literate manner. (B.G.).

decline to take seriously, simply because, if the pupil really did ask such a question, it would be a very good thing).

Finally, it should be mentioned that the introduction of 'relative' numbers while preserving the earlier ones in the form of 'absolute' numbers, in addition to contradicting the view taken by mathematical science, and leading to obvious illogicalities, distorts also the dialectic picture of the development of the idea of number. Instead of creating first the thesis (positive numbers), then the antithesis (negative numbers), and finally combining them in the synthesis (rational numbers— following, that is, the classical path of dialectical generalization—in the above approach both thesis and antithesis are asserted simultaneously, neither of them developing out of the preceding line of growth, but both rising up to one side without any essential relation to the preceding stage.

Irrational Numbers

Our methodologists consider on very proper grounds that the introduction of irrational numbers is one of the most responsible problems of the school algebra course. The study of irrational numbers is practically the only part of the whole mathematics course that in the history of mathematics itself grew up in the nineteenth century. It is that essential basis without which whole sections of the school algebra and geometry courses could not be given a proper logical foundation. It is noteworthy as a step forward in the pupils' understanding that can only be compared in its significance and further consequences with the step forward taken by mathematics itself after the foundation of a general theory of irrational numbers.

The problem of introducing irrational numbers consists in making such an extention of the field of real numbers as will permit a well-defined number to be associated with every element in a linear domain, an immediate example of which is provided by the real line. From the geometrical and physical point of view, the problem appears as the need to ascribe a well-defined number (to denote its size) to every value of a quantity varying in a continuous manner. This practical aim of the theory of irrational numbers must be firmly lodged in the pupils' minds. It must never be replaced by more special objectives, such as the desire to give a well-defined answer to the results of all algebraic operations (extraction of roots), since operations of this type lead only to certain classes of irrational numbers, without bringing up the necessity of constructing a general theory. But it was just this approach which characterized the old system of introducing irrational numbers, now rejected by the modern syllabus on account of its logical shortcomings. It is not possible to prove to a student who is accustomed to the thought that each irrational number is associated in its origin with

B

some algebraic operation—even if in addition he is familiar with the idea of an irrational number as the ratio of two incommensurable segments—that the perimeters of polygons inscribed to a given circle approach a limit as the number of sides is repeatedly doubled; nor is it of any assistance to appeal here to an 'axiom' about the existence of a limit for every monotone bounded sequence, simply because from the point of view of such a student, the axiom itself is false: generally speaking, such a limit cannot be found among the numbers connected with radicals, and in his understanding no other numbers exist (in this case a reference to the 'ratio of segments' would be no more than a smokescreen from the logical point of view, an attempt to conceal the problem rather than to solve it). To avoid futility we ought to point out that by no means do we consider it desirable to prove the theorem on the existence of the limit of a monotone bounded sequence in the school course; it is quite in order to state this proposition without proof. But evidently, before taking such a step, it is absolutely necessary that the field of numbers should be extended to a degree which will render the new axiom free from contradictions; it was in just this point that the earlier system of exposition was at fault: at best, after introducing a certain class of irrational numbers in connection with the extraction of roots, there would be some more or less imprecise remark to the effect that new numbers were also introduced in connection with certain other operations, and that these numbers were also called 'irrational'; and at this the matter would be left; the construction of the field of irrational numbers was considered complete.

Mathematics knows very many logically equivalent methods for constructing a theory of irrational numbers, of which the best known are the methods associated with the names of Weierstrass, Cantor and Dedekind. In agreement with the overwhelming majority of comments on this subject, we suggest that none of these theories should be taught in the secondary school. Moreover, it should be admitted frankly that the *theory* of irrational numbers in the full sense of the word cannot be given in the secondary school. If they were to be treated in the school, such moments as the fundamental theorem on the set of real numbers, and even more the definitions and properties of operations on these numbers, would represent an overburdening of the child's understanding which could lead to no good results; at best, and even then with a proper sense of proportion, these questions could serve as a topic for discussion outside the classroom (mathematical circles) in the tenth class. But our programme makes no demands of this sort, limiting itself solely to the *definition of an irrational number*. We would suggest that such a definition really can be given in a form that is both scientifically unimpeachable and at the same time fully within the pupils' understanding; as we saw above, the extreme importance of this circumstance lies in the fact that only an extension of the concept of number to the field of *all* irrational numbers is capable of rendering meaningful and logically accurate a considerable section of the ensuing courses in algebra, geometry, and trigonometry.

The problem of introducing irrational numbers is made considerably easier by coordinating the actions of both algebraic and geometric stimuli. Hence an important factor contributing to a sound and successful mastery of this part of the course is to make the need for an extension to the field of rational numbers felt simultaneously in the algebra and geometry courses; this factor should be taken into account at once in the syllabus.

A natural formal apparatus for the introduction of irrational numbers is, of course, the decimal fraction. As usual, the definition of $\sqrt{2}$ (a number whose square is equal to two) will serve as a first illustration. It is shown in the usual way that the required number cannot be found among the field of rational numbers, but that it would be desirable to introduce such a number in order to measure the length of an interval that can be constructed in a natural way geometrically. To the right of the point zero, mark off an interval having this length on the number axis. This leads to a point which corresponds to none of the rational numbers when these are set out in their usual way along the real axis. The difficulties arising from this are pointed out; mention is made, for example, of the desirability of having a number to characterize every position of a point moving along the real axis, of having a number to measure every distance that it has traversed. For this purpose the rational numbers, as can be seen from the example, are insufficient: in fact any number of further points (of which the simplest is the mid-point of the segment already described) can now be pointed out, none of which can be characterized by a rational number. Later, it would be in order to recall that this is not the first time that we have introduced new numbers when it happened that for some practical purpose or other the old ones were inadequate; evidently, this is the way we should proceed in the present case.

After this one can return to the particular example and in the usual manner construct two series of finite decimal fractions, with increasing numbers of figures beyond the decimal point, whose squares are respectively less than and greater than the number two. Then the decisive step occurs: we bring in a new number to measure the interval concerned; we show that it is natural to represent this number by an infinite decimal fraction; we show that this fraction cannot be periodic; and finally (far less important) for brevity we denote this number by $\sqrt{2}$.

We would like to emphasize the importance of keeping exactly to the terminology used here. In distinction to the majority of other authors, we consider there are good grounds for avoiding the phrase 'an irrational number *is* an infinite decimal fraction', and we prefer to say that an irrational number *is represented by* or *is expressed as* such a fraction. The complete identification of the number with the symbol representing it we consider here, as always, to be undesirable; from the philosophical point of view it would represent a distinct tendency to nominalism, and from the mathematical point of view it would lead to confusion, since we can use different algorithms for representing one and the same number; this alone is enough to indicate the impossibility of identifying a number with this or that algorithm used to represent it.

After the introduction of the irrational number has been carried out for the example, it is possible to proceed at once to the general definition, repeating the whole construction for any point of the real line not characterized by a rational number. It is then necessary to give a converse argument, with the aim of persuading the pupils that every aperiodic infinite decimal fraction corresponds to a unique irrational number (a unique point without a rational label) which is represented by this fraction. After this, all irrational numbers have been defined, the foundations of the edifice are laid. The mathematical quality of this definition is best of all demonstrated by the fact that starting from this definition it is possible to prove rigorously all the theorems about irrational numbers, to define operations on these numbers, and to establish the properties of these operations. And there can be no doubt as to its being within the pupils' range, especially if it is accompanied by a consistent use of geometrical illustrations.

As was stated above, it is essentially beyond the scope of the secondary schools to take the study of irrational numbers any further. Only the most primitive facts concerning operations on the irrational numbers should be mentioned to the pupils (thus, it would be possible to illustrate the addition of two infinite decimal fractions by an example, and to indicate the geometrical interpretation of the sum of any two positive real numbers as giving the length of a composite interval in terms of the lengths of its components). But it must be pointed out to the pupils with exceptional clarity that all the algebraic operations can be defined for irrational numbers in a meaningful way and that it is proved in higher mathematics that for such operations all those properties are preserved which hold for operations on rational numbers.

Complex Numbers
The last extension of the number concept which concerns the secondary school is the introduction of complex numbers. This problem also presents considerable difficulties from the methodological point view; however, these difficulties are of a quite different nature than in the case of the irrational numbers. There, the factual relevance of the new

numbers, and by the same token their factual meaning, was quite clear and could be fully communicated to the pupils' understanding; the whole difficulty lay in the logical complexity and difficulty of the theory, in particular in the definition and study of operations on the new numbers. Here we have exactly the opposite picture: the definitions of the operations on complex numbers are simple and natural, the study of the properties of these operations presents no conceptual difficulties and, in the formal sense, is not arduous; on the other hand the connections of these numbers with actual reality is a topic whose full treatment can hardly be attempted within the limits of the school course; hence in setting out the theory of complex numbers we must reckon with the danger that in the schoolchildren's minds this whole section will take on the impression of a formal or logical game having no connection with the real world.

It must be admitted openly that such a state of affairs can only be remedied to a certain extent within the bounds of the secondary schools; those pupils whose mathematical education will cease with the school course can of necessity only hear at second hand of the immediate practical applications of the theory of complex numbers, and will never see these applications with their own eyes. Nevertheless it is quite possible to make a fight to create a firm impression in the pupils' minds that the introduction of complex numbers has a solid scientific basis, and this can be done along several different lines. Here we are aided by the circumstance that the pupils have already reached a more mature stage in their mathematical development. If in the sixth and seventh classes the pupils are capable of sensing as necessary and real only those things which have *immediate* practical results and applications, by the tenth class they are already in a position to understand and appreciate the needs of mathematics itself, as being an indirect manifestation of the needs and demands of the same practical world; such a gain as the universal solubility of inverse operations or of certain types of simple equations will already appear as a sensible achievement to the minds of children in the upper classes, and this fact must be exploited as far as possible in the introduction of complex numbers.

The geometrical interpretation of complex numbers serves as another most important weapon in aiding the pupil to link these numbers with a whole series of concrete images. We cannot agree with those who insist on a full geometrization of the theory of complex numbers—i.e. such a treatment of the theory as would define complex numbers and the operations on them directly in geometrical terms—since from all points of view it is better that complex numbers should first of all enter the pupils' minds as an object of arithmetic, i.e. as a new extension of the concept of number, and not as a symbol for a certain geometrical transformation only incidentally having some connections with arithmetic. The geometrical illustration must be what it is, namely, an illustration. But this illustration can be used in the widest manner for giving a concrete form to the idea of a complex number in the pupils' minds, and for linking this idea with a series of simple visual concepts. Taken in conjunction with the role played by complex numbers in the extraction of roots and the solution of equations of higher degree, their geometrical interpretation, allowing them to be used as an analytic apparatus for the simplest operations on vectors, must help to strengthen in the pupils' minds the picture of complex numbers as of no isolated theoretical concept but on the contrary a mathematical object linked with the very firmest threads to a whole series of real algebraic and geometrical questions.

Further, it is necessary to take into account that the very possibility of carrying out on complex numbers all those algebraic operations which are possible with real numbers, while at the same time preserving all the basic properties of these operations, must already create in the mind of a properly educated pupil of the tenth class some picture of the new numbers as valid objects of arithmetic, that is, as a valid extension of the concept of number. That operational principle of which we spoke in the introduction to this article, if it has been sufficiently systematically brought to the pupils' attention, can here reap a definite harvest; it goes without saying that conversely the study of complex numbers must wherever possible be used to strengthen that principle in the pupils' minds.

Finally, we would consider it useful if the teacher, without pretending to provide a basis for his remarks, mentioned that the further development of the theory of complex numbers finds most important applications in the natural sciences and technology, in particular in studying the movements of liquids and gases, in electrical technology, and in aircraft design. If such comments do not enrich the pupils' understanding with any concrete knowledge, at least they are capable of increasing their respect for, and at the same time their attention to and interest in, the subject being studied, which alone is a considerable gain.

In addition to its purely mathematical significance, the introduction of complex numbers appears as almost the clearest illustration in the whole school course of the dialectical growth of mathematical concepts —an illustration which must be all the more fully utilized because by this stage the pupils have already reached an age where they can be given some elementary knowledge of the laws of dialectics.

The complex number, in its first form a purely imaginary number as opposed to a real number (set out along mutually perpendicular axes in the geometrical illustration), in its final form passes over into a general concept where both the real numbers (thesis) and the complex numbers (antithesis) enter as different types; each of the two opposite concepts fully retains its specific features in this synthesis, and enters into a many-sided relationship with its antithesis (every complex number being a particular realization of this relation). All this does not hinder the aggregate of such relations (combinations of real and purely imaginary) from forming a unified and elegant whole—the world of complex numbers—which finds its visual illustration in the final, completed version of the complex plane. It would hardly be possible to find another example where the dialectical laws pertaining to the growth of mathematical concepts could be illustrated in such completeness.

Directing the pupils' attention to the dialectical picture just described is all the more desirable in that its effect may be not purely philosophical—it may also have concrete mathematical content. Considerations of this kind are capable, for example, of strengthening the pupil's conception of a real number as one type, a particular case, of a complex number (in distinction to the incorrect but quite widespread view which holds that by its nature a complex number cannot be real). It is quite evident that for the achievement of this purpose impeccably exact terminology is needed; the pupils must be thoroughly accustomed to calling the number $a + b\sqrt{-1}$ (where a and b are real)

(1) complex — for arbitrary a and b;
(2) real — for $b = 0$;
(3) imaginary — for $b \neq 0$;
(4) purely imaginary — for $a = 0$, $b \neq 0$.[1]

Correspondingly, the pupils must be able to determine quickly from the position of a point on the complex plane what sort of a number corresponds to it; i.e. must know whereabouts in the plane the real, imaginary, and purely imaginary numbers lie.

There should be no need to stress that the list of terms set out above is not strictly a *classification*, since the listed classes of numbers are in general not mutually exclusive.

---

[1]This suggestion of A. Ya. Khinchin's has been taken up and is inserted as an explanatory note to the syllabus. See, for example, 'The syllabus of the secondary schools for the 1962/63 school year, Mathematics.' Uchpedgiz, 1962, p. 9 (B.G.).

Section 2: The Concept of Limit

Historical Summary

As with the majority of mathematical concepts, the modern concept of limit was not created at once, but underwent a long evolution from its crude beginnings to the form encountered in present-day mathematics. In a first look at this evolutionary process, we can distinguish four major determining stages.

The first stage, the longest, covers the seventeenth and eighteenth centuries and is associated with the period of the initial, turbulent, and uncritical development of infinitesimal analysis. This was the period of rapid accumulation of factual material and particular, concrete results; as is usual in such periods, scholars paid relatively little attention to the analysis and exact definitions of fundamental concepts; thus it is hardly possible to point now to a formulation of the concept of limit that would cover all the ways in which the term was understood at that time; one can attempt only to sketch in some general features of the idea of limit typical of the mathematics of that period.

In any epoch, the concept of limit depends vitally upon what is understood by the term 'infinitesimal'. In the period we are considering, there was neither full clarity nor full agreement as to the nature of infinitesimals. Although the dynamic origin of infinitesimals, their association with the development of some process, was not in doubt, the idea of a variable itself was so new, still taken up so uncertainly by mathematics, that the term 'infinitesimal' was largely understood in the sense of a reference to the dimensions of a quantity, and not as a reference to the manner in which the quantity changes; it was customary to make use of such descriptive phrases as 'the shadow of a quantity', 'the spirit of a quantity', etc. If an attempt is made to express this idea in exact terminology, then it has to be acknowledged that by an infinitesimal was understood a quantity which was less than any positive number in absolute value, and yet distinct from zero. The variable nature of the quantity was in this way expressed only indirectly, and in the consciousness of the epoch could not be adequately formulated in exact, logical terms. Consequently the concept of limit remained from the logical point of view one of statics, concerned essentially with 'actual' (i.e. constant) numbers of infinitely small size. Although there can be no doubt that the logical weaknesses of this picture troubled the outstanding minds of the period, it endured over a very long time;

what is more, it occasionally reappears even to-day, in the applied sciences (the concept of 'differential' in mechanics) and in certain textbooks (see for example the course in mathematical analysis by Professor Vygodski—although justice demands we acknowledge that here the author fully admits that his presentation is archaic and uses it deliberately as a pedagogical device). The reason why the idea of an infinitesimal (and, therefore, the idea of limit) endured for so long in a logically unfinished form is in part to be found in the style of the epoch, as mentioned above, which was so fully occupied with the rapid building of the edifice of mathematical analysis that there was little time to spare for a thorough study of its foundations; but there is a further, more significant reason. As was subsequently pointed out with great clarity by Engels, the inclusion of the idea of a *variable* as an object of research within the scope of mathematical science, required the elements of dialectical thought, and this was evidently never within the scope of the described epoch. Thus a situation arose where the dynamic character of the infinitesimal, and of the limit process, was not consciously recognized, but had to remain outside the walls of precise mathematical formulation, being admitted to the formulation we have described only as an illustrative supplement, not pretending to exactitude.

This first stage in the evolution of the limit concept must by now be regarded as completely outgrown, and any return to it as an appearance of reactionary tendencies.

The second stage in the growth of the concept of limit corresponds roughly to the first half of the nineteenth century. It must be acknowledged as the most important step forward taken by this concept throughout its whole history. In this period creative scholars were already paying sufficient attention to questions concerning the foundations of analysis for there to be a real possibility of overcoming the basic logical defect of which we have already spoken. The way in which this defect was overcome depended essentially on the fact that the idea of a variable was by now firmly lodged among the ranks of precisely formulated mathematical concepts; thus it was possible to include the idea of change in the definition of limit, i.e. to restore to this concept its original dynamic meaning, and in so doing to avoid those logical mute points which were characteristic of the preceding epoch. By this period it had already been clearly stated that an infinitesimal is a quantity which at a given stage in the process under consideration becomes, and in all its further stages *remains*, arbitrarily small in absolute value (smaller than an arbitrary positive number). Without doubt this association with a process, this dynamic essence of the concept of an infinitesimal (and of course of the corresponding concept of limit), was clear to many even during the preceding period; but *its explicit incorporation in the formal definition* of limit required a really significant evolution in mathematical thinking, the inclusion of a new dialectical element, and is indubitably one of the greatest achievements of this epoch, being associated with the names of Cauchy, Abel, and other scholars.

It is just this definition of an infinitesimal which shows so clearly that the term 'infinitesimal' does not refer to its dimensions (an infinitesimal can sometimes be extremely large) but to *the way in which it changes*. In this sense the term 'infinitesimal', created at an earlier period, is an obvious anachronism; it would be more appropriate to exchange it for the term 'indefinitely decreasing' quantity, or some such analogous phrase. Unfortunately, this has not happened, and every teacher will know how many difficulties and errors are created through this unfortunate use of words.

So far as questions relating to secondary school teaching are concerned, it is exceedingly important to note that despite the further development of the limit concept, of which we shall say more below, modern mathematics in no way rejects the picture formed in this period. Modern mathematics makes this picture *more precise* and *more general*, but it has not changed it at any point, in contrast to the case of the picture accepted in the seventeenth and eighteenth centuries, which modern mathematics considers inadequate for the reasons set out earlier.

The third stage is associated with the second half of the nineteenth century. It is closely connected with both the general tendency to formalize mathematics, and the narrower objective of arithmetizing analysis, i.e. of reducing its foundations to the natural numbers. It was in this period that rigorous theories of irrational numbers were first constructed (Dedekind, Cantor) and, on this basis, that the foundations of infinitesimal analysis were laid (Weierstrass and others).

It is well known that without a full theory of irrational numbers, it is not possible to provide an adequate foundation for the study of limits, or to give an exact meaning to the definitions of the classical constants π and e. Without the general definition of an irrational number, fundamental theorems (for example, the theorem on the existence of the limit of a monotone bounded quantity) are either untrue or devoid of meaning; at the same time these theorems are quite essential even within the bounds of the school course. It should be pointed out that the introduction of such theorems into the school course as postulates not requiring proof in no way saves the situation. The basic difficulty consists not so much in the impossibility of proving these theorems as in the fact that their very content, without some previous general definition of irrational numbers, is either false or meaningless. Thus, for someone who is not acquainted with the general concept of an irrational number, the assertion that a monotone bounded quantity has a limit (no matter whether it is introduced as a postulate or a theorem) can only be understood in one of two senses: either in the sense that the limit exists in that class of numbers with which he is already acquainted (which is evidently false) or that there is no clearly defined field in view, in which case the assertion loses any precise content.

Thus, if from a conceptual point of view the idea of limit was reasonably well-formulated in the first half of the nineteenth century, there nevertheless remained considerable gaps which were only filled in during the second half of the century.

At the same time, the growing demands to formalize mathematics required a new edition of the formal definition of the limit concept—without, however, changing its intuitive content. In the earlier definition of infinitesimal there was still, whether explicitly or no, some recollection of the real process from which the given quantity was derived, and of the different stages in this process. The new edition gave expression to the demand for a full formalization of this side of the definition. In fact it was in this epoch that the infinitesimal (and, indeed, every quantity tending to a limit) came to be understood as a function of one or more independent variables, and the reference to the real process to be replaced by a formal description of the behaviour of these variables. The expression '$y \to b$' by itself now became devoid of meaning, and only expressions of the type '$y \to b$ as $x \to a$' were given any specific content. This content is formalized as follows: '$|y - b|$ is arbitrarily small whenever $|x - a|$ is sufficiently small', or, even more precisely, 'no matter how small $\varepsilon > 0$, there exists a $\delta > 0$ such that $|y - b| < \varepsilon$ whenever $|x - a| < \delta$' (this last formulation is found almost unchanged in reputable analysis courses of the present day).

Such is the extent to which the earlier reference to the real process and its various stages has become formalized. Outwardly, nothing remains in this last definition of the initial picture linking the idea of a limit to the development of some process; the lively, dynamic image of passage to the limit has as it were been exchanged for a motionless, purely static *relation* between certain regions of values of the independent variable and the corresponding regions of values of the dependent variable. This outwardly static character of the concept of limit, as it appears in modern mathematics, often gives rise to the objection that, having frozen the movement out of the idea of limit, it thereby creates a tendency to dissociate the mathematical concept of limit from the living reality whose reflection and abstraction it is supposed to represent. This criticism is *essentially* invalid, because the modern definition at no point contradicts the earlier one, but merely refines it, and therefore cannot have a different content. More important for us, however, is that from the *pedagogical* point of view, the objection raised in this criticism deserves every attention. A very high level of mathematical culture is needed in order not to lose sight of the original, dynamic picture of passage to the limit in a definition which, in the process of logical analysis, has been taken to the final stage of dissection and acquired a static form. There is a real danger that someone without a fluent mastery of the typical steps in modern, complex mathematical thought will, in fact, lose the connection between the concept of limit and the real source from which the concept arose and whose reflection in abstract mathematical terms it is supposed to represent.

The fourth and final stage in the growth of the limit concept already takes us into our own century, and is connected with the long-evident necessity of significantly widening the idea embodied in the initial concept. Long previously, mathematicians had found it necessary to study limit processes in regions of quite different structure from the simplest case where the variable quantity is a real number: limits of complex numbers, limits of multi-dimensional vectors, limits of functions, limits of random variables (in probability theory). In the more complex cases it had seemed appropriate to introduce several types of limit process; thus, in the case of the limit of functions, a distinction was made between ordinary convergence, uniform convergence, convergence 'in the mean', etc. and naturally, these different limit processes possessed different specific properties. This circumstance, together with the tendency towards generalization characteristic of the mathematics of our own epoch, led to the creation of general theories of limit processes. Here it is not a question of the limit of a variable in the narrow sense of the word, i.e. of the limit of a variable real number; the object that tends to the limit, as well as the limit itself, can have any particular meaning. The general study of limits makes a complete abstraction from the particular context, and takes as its sole object of study the structure of the limit process itself. To a large extent, such is the concept of limit in modern *topology* (the general study of continuous transformations) and in modern *generalized analysis*.

We shall not stop to consider in any more detail this new and important idea in the history of the limit concept, since, despite its significance in mathematical science, there can be no doubt whatsoever that it is not only outside the scope of the school course itself, but hardly capable of exerting even an indirect influence on its programme or style of teaching. We mention only (and this is important for our purposes) that in this fourth stage, as in the third, the concept of limit worked out in the second stage is in no way altered or rejected. If towards the end of the nineteenth century it underwent refinement and extension, in our century it has been greatly generalized and carried to a higher level of abstraction; but in neither the one case nor the other has that concept been rejected.

The Picture of Limit in the School[1]

In selecting the form of the limit concept which will be most effective for school-teaching purposes, we must, as always, take into account two principal requirements:

(1) this form should in no point contradict the traditions of modern science;

(2) it should be sufficiently concrete for the new concept not to be divorced in the schoolchild's mind from the real phenomena it is designed to represent.

The preceding historical summary shows clearly that so far as the concept of limit is concerned, the second problem (which in other cases may present considerable difficulties) is here solved quite simply. First of all it must be admitted that the first form of the limit concept, which we characterized in describing the first stage, is wholly unsuitable: it fails to satisfy either requirement. On the one hand it has been definitely superseded and rejected by modern science as logically inadequate; on the other hand the dynamic character of the limit process is at least pushed into the background, so that the link with real phenomena is veiled over and logically imprecise. If the schoolchild leaves school with a picture of an infinitesimal as of something insignificantly small, unworthy of attention—or even worse, as some type of weird number which is smaller than any positive number and yet not zero—then the problems of the higher schools will be greatly complicated; before taking such a student any further in his development they will have to deal with the problem of how to blow out of his mind concepts and habits which stand in contradiction to modern scientific opinion.

One is hardly likely to encounter any objections to the view that those extensions to the limit concept that we indicated in describing the fourth stage could not form part of the school course; too general a concept of limit would, in the first place, find no applications in the school course, and in the second would represent such a degree of abstraction as could hardly be within the schoolchild's grasp.

Many teachers have put forward the view that if we understand by limit only the limit of a real variable, then with this restriction the school formulation should be taken right up to its modern scientific wording. This means that the limit concept should be given in terms of a relation between $\varepsilon-$ and $\delta-$ regions. We must assert quite definitely that we consider this form to be unsuitable. Even as regards acquiring a purely formal mastery of the definition, many years' experience has shown that this form gives rise to very considerable

---

[1]In text-books of mathematical analysis it is now customary to give the following definition of the limit of a sequence: 'the quantity a_n tends to the limit a if no matter how small the number $\varepsilon > 0$, there exists a positive integer n_ε such that for any $n > n_\varepsilon$ the inequality $|a_n - a| < \varepsilon$ holds true'. (B.G.).

and sometimes insurmountable difficulties, and not only with school-children, but also with students in the early courses at the higher schools. Even if we concede that in particular cases an experienced teacher may, with a considerable expenditure of time and effort, succeed in getting his pupils to overcome the formal difficulties associated with this definition, it is still a matter well beyond a schoolchild's powers to link this formal scheme with actual limit processes in real phenomena; thus the concept of limit if formulated in this way will be mastered at best abstractly, at the price of a large gulf between the concept itself and the real considerations with which it is associated. Taking a different point of view, there is really no need for such a definition. If, by the words 'in the given process the variable x has as its limit the constant value a' (in symbols lim x = a, or x $\rightarrow$ a) the pupil is accustomed to understand the fact that starting from some moment (a certain stage) of the process, the difference $|x - a|$ becomes, and at all later stages remains, as small as we please, then this definition (corresponding to the second stage in our historical summary) will satisfy all the necessary requirements. In the first place it in no way contradicts modern mathematical formulations, and the higher schools, on taking into their corpus a schoolchild having this picture of a limit, would have no difficulty in extending this idea and making it more precise. Nothing would have to be 'blown out', nothing taken away from what the child had learned in secondary school. And in the second place it is this definition more than any of the others (either its successors or its predecessors), which stands closest to the real phenomena that are the natural objects of its application.

However, while insisting that for school purposes the definition we have advocated is in all respects the most effective, we certainly do not wish to assert that the redoubtable number ε should be driven out of school-teaching. Thus, in proving the theorem about the sum and product of infinitesimals, the introduction of an arbitrarily small constant ε seems to us quite appropriate. The discussion leading up to these theorems would indeed be a convenient place to explain to the pupils that the notation $|x - a| < \varepsilon$, where ε is an arbitrarily small fixed quantity, exactly symbolizes the expression contained in the definition of limit, that 'in the course of the process the difference $|x - a|$ becomes and remains as small as we please in absolute value'. We would even allow, if the general level of the class was sufficiently high, that in the definition itself it would be possible to use the more sophisticated expression 'the difference x − a (becomes and remains in the course of the given process) smaller in absolute value than any arbitrary positive constant', although there is no doubt that such a form leads to greater difficulties if it is to be properly understood and mastered. But we consider that the reference to the real process and its different stages should under no circumstance be replaced in the definition (as it is in modern text-books by way of further formalization) by a discussion of the region of values of the independent variable defining the course of the process; or at least it would be improper to do so in general discussions at the first stage of study (later on, while looking at particular concrete examples, it might be very useful to study the range of values of such an independent variable, as we shall see below).

Let us clarify our point of view by an example. Suppose that we were discussing how, as $n \to \infty$, the apothem[1], a_n, of a regular n-gon inscribed to a given circle has as its limit the radius of the circle, r. We should most prefer that the content of this phrase be expressed by the words 'the difference $|r - a_n|$ becomes and remains arbitrarily small as n increases without limit'; we should consider somewhat less desirable (because it is harder to master) but still quite acceptable the formulation 'no matter what the arbitrary positive constant ε, the difference $|r - a_n|$ becomes and remains less than ε as n increases without limit'; finally, we should consider as quite unacceptable the formulation, 'no matter what the positive constant ε, there exists a whole number N (depending on ε) such that $|r - a_n|$ is less than ε whenever $n > N$'. To avoid obvious inconsistencies, we must agree here that everything we have said above refers only to the general definition of the concept of limit, to the verbal formulation of the picture that the schoolchild must learn to associate with the term 'limit'. At a later stage, by way of concrete work on particular examples, it is not only desirable but essential to give a full illustration, carried out right up to the calculations themselves, of the references to the different stages of the process contained in the general definition. Thus, returning to our example, we consider that it would be quite in order to set the pupils the question 'how large must we take the number n in order that the difference $|r - a_n|$ should be less than 0·01, 0·001, etc.' Such examples not only strengthen the link between theory and application, but create the basis for an easier mastery of the more formal, general concept of limit in the future.

In mathematical analysis itself, as in its different applications, a basic role is played by two definite types of limit process: (1) the limit of the sequence $a_1, a_2, ..., a_n, ...$ as $n \to \infty$; (2) the limit of the function $y = F(x)$ as x tends to the constant number a. In the secondary schools it is usual to attempt to embrace both types both in the general definition and in the choice of examples. This attempt leads to wellknown difficulties, since the two types differ sufficiently for the schoolchild, on his first acquaintance with the concept of limit, to have some trouble

---

[1]The perpendicular distance from the centre to one of the sides.

in recognizing their common features and accepting them as parts of a single whole. The differences, of course, have their root in the behaviour of the independent variable characterizing the process; in the first case, this variable (n) takes on only positive integral values; in the second (x) a continuous range of values; in the first case n increases without limit; in the second x tends to a finite limit. In this respect it is important to point out that the definition of limit that we have recommended includes both cases equally, just because the character of the different stages remains unformalized in this definition, while the two types described differ precisely in the manner of this formalization. All definitions of a more formal type that are thinkable in the context of the secondary school (and, indeed, of the first courses of the higher schools) inevitably come up against a new difficulty: different definitions are required for both types of limit process, and this, of course, renders still more difficult an understanding of the single common logical and factual content of these two cases[1].

Methodological Remarks

In this way it seems to us that the main problem in teaching the theory of limits in the secondary schools is to create a sound and accurate picture of the limit process which will correspond in its essential ideas to the concept of limit as it is understood in modern mathematical analysis; however, it is not necessary, and in many cases would even be harmful, to take the limit concept to that stage of formal logical analysis which is typical of the modern mathematical treatment.

Evidently, such an assessment of the aims of the teaching process must have a decisive influence on our whole approach to the methodology of the relevant chapters—on the selection and arrangement of material, the style of exposition, and so on. Of course, we cannot give here a full methodological treatment of these chapters. Our purpose is to gather together a few particular remarks of a methodological character which arise from the statement of aims set out above. In doing so, we shall naturally focus the reader's attention on those places in the traditional exposition where it seems to us necessary to introduce certain changes and corrections.

A precise, concrete picture of a complex phenomenon, involving

---

[1]We should, however, point out that there is every possibility of limiting the school course to a narrower idea of limit, by completely excluding from consideration the second of the two types mentioned; the fact is that only the limit of a sequence occurs in all such applications of the concept of limit as are likely to be found in the secondary school course; this is the case with infinite decimal fractions in the theory of irrational numbers, in the study of progressions and in all geometrical applications. As for the limit of a function, this will be needed only in such parts of the theory of equations and of functional dependence as are studied in our secondary schools by way of rare exceptions.

many variable quantities which change in quite different ways, will be most easily lodged in the pupils' minds through a thorough, many-sided discussion of a single such phenomenon. The example chosen for such a study must be on the one hand reasonably obvious and close to the pupil's understanding, and on the other hand sufficiently precise to serve as the base on which an accurate picture can be built up in the pupil's mind, and to allow the performance of detailed calculations. Perhaps geometrical processes best answer these requirements. If, for example, we choose as our initial illustration the continued doubling of the number of sides of a regular polygon inscribed to a given circle, and if we study this process in all its details, then the pupils will have directly in front of them a large number of variable quantities behaving in quite different ways and all involved in one and the same process: the length of the side, the size of the interior angle, the size of the exterior angle, the perimeter, the apothem, the sum of the interior angles, the sum of the exterior angles, and so on; here there are quantities both infinitely small and infinitely large; and constants; and quantities with positive limits. There are not the slightest grounds for begrudging time spent on a detailed study of one example, for the educative effect of such a study far exceeds what could be achieved by considering a large number of miscellaneous and artificial examples with no obvious interpretation. We would underline in particular the significance of the fact that all the variable quantities studied in a single example are participants in one and the same process; their changes are mutually coordinated, functionally inter-dependent; even if this circumstance is not explicitly pointed out by the teacher, prolonged concentration on a complex, concrete process will certainly have a significant educative effect, leading the pupils to associate mentally the abstract concepts of the theory of limits with complex and varied processes of the real world.

In this connection we should like to suggest that in general the teacher keep to the essential minimum the number of examples not connected with the factual material of the course and therefore having an artificial character. To say nothing of geometry, so much material for examples and problems is provided by the theory of progressions, of decimal fractions, of irrational numbers, that there can hardly be a great need for a large number, of exercises thought up especially for the purpose and not having any real, tangible content. However, even that small number which is considered essential should not be selected at random, but chosen with proper relevance; they should always concern the limiting behaviour of an analytical expression that is in some way typical or instructive and hence likely to be of value in the future. As an example, we might suggest at least the study of the ratio of two polynomials as the independent variable increases without bound; it would be a good thing if the pupils were able to indicate immediately, without calculation, the limits as x → ∞ of such expressions as

$$\frac{x}{1 + x} \quad \text{or} \quad \frac{3x^2 - 5}{4x^2 - 2x + 7}.$$

In defining new concepts, and in formulating and proving new theorems, the dynamic character of passage to the limit should be emphasized unremittingly, always with the necessary reference to the process and its different stages, and always demanding from the pupil a clear understanding of this aspect of the problem. He should understand clearly that 0·000,000,000,1 is not an infinitisimal; and that, on the contrary, the distance from the earth of a meteorite destined to fall on to the earth *is* an infinitesimal, even though at a given time that distance might amount to a colossal number of kilometers. The pupil must understand firmly that a quantity is an infinitesimal only in given circumstances, within the scope of some particular process, and that in a different process the very same quantity might change in a different fashion. The pupil should know that a variable can approach its limit either from below, i.e. from the region of smaller values (increasing), or from above (decreasing), or from both sides (oscillating), and that in the last case it may pass through its limit value even before the process is completed. Without a fluent mastery of all these and similar ideas, the study of limits can be at best a theory that has been formally understood but whose essential content has been missed.

Finally, it is necessary to say a few words about notation and terminology. It is absolutely essential that along with the traditional notation lim x = a, the pupils should have fully mastered the notation x → a for the same assertion, since each year the latter will be encountered more and more frequently in analysis and its applications. It is correct to write not lim y = b, but lim y = b, and correspondingly to read not
       x = a   x → a
'for x equal to a', but 'as x tends towards a'. The notation 'n → ∞' should be read as 'for n increasing without bound', or at least it is quite essential that the pupils should have firmly grasped the fact that n here does not tend to any limit. Finally, the teacher should point out that the symbol 'lim' is deduced from the Latin word 'limes' (limit) (the frequently encountered assertion that this symbol is derived from the French word 'limite' is based on an evident misconception, for with equal justice we might as well assert that it was derived from the corresponding English, Italian, Spanish etc. term)[1].

[1]The symbol 'lim' is used internationally, in Russian texts as well as in English,
       x → a
although the Russians have their own word 'predel' meaning 'limit'. (trans.).

Section 3: The Concept of Functional Dependence

I

To some degree almost all contemporary methodologists uphold the view that the concept of functional dependence ought to be not only one of the most important topics in the school mathematics course, but that fundamental axis leading from elementary arithmetic to the higher branches of algebra, geometry and trigonometry around which all mathematics teaching should be grouped. This view can, of course, be taken too far: there is a distinct danger that its uncritical adoption would cause other concepts, approaches, and methods—no less important in themselves—to be undervalued: the concept of number, basic algebraic operations and geometric structures, etc. If correctly understood, however, accompanied by sufficient pedagogical tact, and applied with a proper sense of proportion, there is no doubt that the asserted thesis can serve to point out a proper and fruitful path for the syllabus compiler, methodologist and teacher.

For what reason, then, is the concept of functional dependence given such an exceptional role; why is it expressly singled out from all the other mathematical concepts with which the secondary school acquaints its pupils?

Because, first, no other concept reflects the phenomena of the real world with such directness and concreteness as that of functional dependence, which alone embodies the mobility and dynamism of the real world, and the inter-dependence of real quantities.

Because, second, this concept illustrates as does no other the dialectical features of modern mathematical thought: it is just the concept of functional dependence that can teach the child to think of quantities in their real variability and not in an artificially devised immobility; in their mutual connections and interdependence, and not in a state of artificial isolation from each other.

Because, finally, the concept of functional dependence is fundamental to higher mathematics, and therefore the extent to which children leaving school are well-prepared for the mathematics courses in the higher institutes is to a large extent determined by how firm, full, and cultured is their grasp of this most important concept.

II

In our school programmes, the study of functions is divided off into a special topic of the algebra course. It is evident from the description of this topic in the syllabus that only one, relatively narrow, problem is there in view: to teach the children how to represent functions by graphs. This is indeed how the aim of this topic should be understood. But, of course, this should not be taken to mean that efforts to master the concept of functional dependence and to acquire the technique of functional thinking can be limited to the study of this special topic. On the contrary, the idea of functional dependence can only take its place in the pupil's mind as a firm, familiar, and active element, as a tool of mathematical thought, if it is studied systematically throughout the whole duration of the mathematics course, from elementary arithmetic to the higher branches of algebra and trigonometry. We do not mean, of course, that it would be in order to give a general definition of function in the early classes, or even that the term 'function' itself should be used, thrust down the pupils' throats, at every suitable opportunity. This is not the case at all. By all means let the pupils hear the word 'function' only in the later classes, let it be at a more mature stage that they first think over what role the study of the mutual relations of quantities plays in our picture of the real world; no clearly formulated general propositions, and in particular no abstract definitions or special terms, are needed in the early and middle classes of the secondary school. The habit of functional thinking must be cultivated quite unforcedly, without the children realizing it, without burdening their minds with abstractions beyond their grasp, and yet persistently, continually, day by day. The teacher must give some thought to it in every lesson—there is material to be found in any topic in arithmetic, algebra or geometry that will direct the pupils' attention to the particular side of the question under study which they will later come to recognize as a functional dependence between quantities. The effect of changing the components of an arithmetical operation on the result of the operation, the first formulae using letters, the first quantitative relations in geometry, the first acquaintance with equations—all this and much more yields inexhaustible material for simple questions, which are very far from overtaxing the pupils' attention, but which systematically set them to think how one quantity is changed by the changes in another quantity; on how many and precisely which other quantities the quantity defined by some formula depends; how many and precisely which elements of a triangle must be known in order to determine uniquely all its elements, etc. In order to determine the area of a square, it is sufficient to know one length (the side or diagonal etc.); the same for the area of a circle; but to determine the area of a rectangle or triangle two lengths must be known. In order to determine a rational number it is sufficient to give a finite set of digits, but to determine an irrational number an infinite set must be given. If the first figure after the decimal point in a decimal fraction is altered, the size of the fraction changes appreciably; however, if we alter the sixth figure after the decimal point, the value of the fraction is almost unchanged. If one side of a triangle is rotated uniformly about a vertex, its point of intersection with the other side will alter slowly at first, but later, with a colossal speed. On increasing the number of sides of a right polygon the interior angle increases (quickly at first but more slowly later) while the exterior angle decreases. The root of the equation $ax = b$ (where $a \neq 0$, $b \neq 0$) decreases when a increases, but increases when b increases (in both cases without bound). The expression $n!$ grows very rapidly as n increases; n^3 grows more rapidly than n^2 but 2^n grows more rapidly than either.

All these and countless similar elementary remarks and questions, supported by the appropriate simple calculations and practised systematically, at every opportunity, aim at leading the pupil to the stage where, when the time comes for him to take in the general idea of functional dependence, he will be well prepared not only for the purely formal aspects of the new concept, but for its real, factual content, and the ideas and techniques associated with it.

While placing a high value on the preparatory teaching of functional dependence as described above, we must of course, take care that at the same time the sections of the school course that provide opportunities for studying the most important special functions are covered in a way that gives proper weight to the functional aspect of the question.

It is quite inadmissable for the pupils to study quadratic equations without acquiring a detailed understanding of the behaviour of a trinomial of the second degree as one of the simplest and most important functions. Here, as in other cases, it often happens that the demands of the syllabus are understood only formally: the pupils are taught to construct parabolas by rule, and that is the end of the matter. The graph, which by its nature is a visual tool allowing some of the most important features of the studied functional dependence to be picked out directly from a geometrical image, is turned from a means into an end; in the long run this completely distorts the methodological situation. In passing, if the pupil does not use the image of a parabola to solve problems on the maxima and minima of trinomials of the second degree, for drawing quick conclusions as to the nature of the growth and decay of the function (where it increases and where it decreases, where it increases more rapidly, where less rapidly, etc.), the number and locations of its roots and so on, then the study of graphs has become an almost purposeless exercise, from which all the real content has been dropped.

The above remarks apply even more strongly to the study of the logarithmic and exponential functions. It is widely known that pupils who have a thorough mastery of the technique of calculating with logarithms, who can readily solve logarithmic and exponential equations, nevertheless have so poor an understanding of the nature of a logarithm that the problem 'find without the aid of tables the number $10^{\lg 7}$' causes them real difficulties; the question of the functional nature of the logarithm remains, of course, even further beyond their grasp, even if they have studied how to draw the graph of this function. Here we must say this: if the pupil is not accustomed to linking with the graph of the logarithmic function such questions as the increase of the logarithm as compared with the increase of the number, the relative rate of this increase at different parts of the number axis, the fact that numbers smaller than unity have negative logarithms, the intersection of all logarithmic curves at a single point as an illustration of the property $\lg_a 1 = 0$ for arbitrary $a < 0$, etc., then his acquaintance with the graph of the logarithmic function must remain to a large extent useless. This defect in our school teaching shows up as none other than one of its chief general weaknesses—the formal study of each topic at the expense of its real content.

Such remarks can be applied with equal justification to the study of (direct and inverse) trigonometric functions; here also logarithmic calculations, the solution of triangles and trigonometric equations, overshadow and push into the background precisely those aspects which, from a conceptual and even from a practical point of view, should be the basic core of all trigonometry: the functional nature of the sine, cosine, etc.

Here also, as a rule, we find that pupils are almost completely lacking in a sound understanding of the periodicity of the trigonometric functions as a fundamental characteristic of their graphs; the signs of these functions in different quadrants, their rates of increase and decrease, are not connected to the graphical images; almost none of the pupils know that the cosine curve can be obtained from the sin curve by a simple translation, and those who have heard of this fact are unable to point out the analytical relation corresponding to the geometrical one.

All the facts indicated, and many others of an analogous type, reflect rather severely on the quality of the pupils' training, and make the subsequent work of the higher schools unnecessarily complicated and more difficult. Given such an approach, the study of the elements of functional dependence cannot achieve a single one of the aims intended by its inclusion in the school course.

What then is needed to combat these defects? The answer to this question follows clearly from what we have said already. No amount of concentration and effort on the special theme 'functions and their graphs' will be of assistance here. In the first place it is necessary that all sections of the mathematics course which precede this topic (and also—let us add—physics and chemistry classes) should be used for a systematic, regular introduction to the study of functional dependence. And in the second place it is necessary that, in studying those sections of the course relating to the most important special functions, the conceptional, functional side of the question should always be made the hub around which the rest is grouped, and not hidden away in the background.

We would suggest that all the remarks needed for this purpose should find a place in the syllabus (which would not necessarily require any change in content) and in the attached explanatory notes.

III

Everything that has been said so far has concerned the role, place, and specific emphasis that should be given to the concept of functional dependence in the school mathematics course. We turn now to the most important question—the *content* of this concept.

The history of the concept of functional dependence in mathematical science is well known, and there is no need for us to set it out here in detail. Different authors from Newton to the present day have formulated this concept in many different ways. The most obvious and for our purposes the most important tendency in the historical development of the concept of functional dependence has been the gradual freeing of this concept from the clutches of a formal apparatus—the mathematical formula—, a development accomplished in the heat of battle, and finally achieved only in the second half of the nineteenth century. When the concept of functional dependence first arose, it was found that the mathematical formula, the analytical expression, made a most excellent tool for its investigation. Faith in this tool was so strong, formulae appeared with such regularity wherever talk of functions sprang up, that soon, as has often happened in mathematics, mathematicians lost sight of the need, and thereby the ability, to distinguish between the mathematical concept and the formal apparatus that had been introduced to analyze and serve it. The function became identified with the analytical expression, and this circumstance was not only a fact of scientific practice, but was upheld by many leading mathematicians as an explicit thesis. However, the opposing current, springing from a more or less consciously recognized principle that it is essential to maintain a strict distinction between the interior content of a mathematical concept and the formal apparatus that serves as its exterior expression, never died right away. As always, life was on the side of the real and not the formal picture, and in the final count it was the real picture which conquered, prohibiting any confusion of the function with the analytical apparatus used to describe it. The formal apparatus, raised to a status which it had no right to assume, had step by step turned itself from a convenient and serviceable tool into a tyrant, paralyzing the idea of functional dependence. After a certain stage, however, the evolving concept of a function could no longer be contained within the narrow bounds of an analytical expression. Although it had long been known that one and the same analytical expression could be used to depict several different functional dependences, now there appeared cases where, conversely, several different analytical expressions came into use for depicting one and the same functional dependence. Sometimes functions came into use for which it was hard to find any analytical expression, and—most important of all—in many cases this analytical expression turned out to be so complicated that it could not be used in studying the function; it became necessary to investigate further, *non-analytical* methods.

In the end, all these and many other facts forced a recognition that the artificial identification of the concept of functional dependence with the analytical apparatus was limiting, holding up, the natural and (for mathematics) essential growth of this concept; that only by completely unloosing the concept of function from the restricting bonds of formulae and analytical expression would it be possible to provide the proper space needed for this concept to grow in answer to the demands of mathematics and the applied sciences. By the middle of last century, this realization had already found expression in that definition of the concept of functional dependence which is usually associated with the name of Dirichlet[1], and which is accepted without dispute in modern mathematics. In this definition there is no mention of an analytical expression, and we have to do with a function whenever it is possible to ascribe to every value of one quantity in a certain domain a corresponding definite value of another quantity. The means by which this correspondence is described has here only a secondary significance, and does not affect the fact of the functional dependence itself. It can be an analytical formula, or a geometrical transformation, or some exhaustive verbal description, etc. Thus, for the well-known 'Dirichlet's function', equal to zero for all rational numbers and to unity for all irrational numbers, it is possible to find analytical expressions in terms of the usual mathematical symbols, but Dirichlet's function does not become any more of a function simply from the fact that such expressions can

---

[1] L. Dirichlet (1805–59)—an outstanding German mathematician (B.G.).

be found. From the modern point of view, it was a fully-fledged function even without the analytical expressions. Moreover, the relatively complicated analytical expressions which can be found for it are hardly capable of helping us in any way to study the properties of this function, and no matter what comes to pass they will remain a scientifically fruitless creation, only worthy to gladden the eyes of a lover of 'analytical expressions'.

Having accepted the definition of a function as a correspondence, mathematics drew from this all necessary conclusions. However, from the cultural and historical point of view, the subsequent implementation of this reform was not such an easy matter; the traditions of the whole many-year preceding period, when the idea of the formula, of the analytical apparatus, prevailed over the idea of the function, suffered extinction only with extreme reluctance; in many cases they are still alive today, and we find their clear traces staring us in the face even in the best modern text books for the higher schools.

It is understandable that the secondary schools, lagging further behind modern science than the higher schools, should suffer from this defect to a greater extent. In practice, all teaching of functions in the secondary schools, although formally based on the modern definitions of the basic concepts, is carried out at a level and in a style which makes it necessary for the higher schools to start their work by correcting a large number of incorrect and unscientific ideas and habits in their students.

Formula-hypnosis appears as a universal evil, so firmly rooted in the students' minds that in the higher schools the first attempts to create a proper understanding of functional dependence sometimes come up against fierce resistance.

The definition of the function

$$y = \begin{cases} \sin x, & \text{if } x \leq 0, \\ \lg x, & \text{if } x > 0 \end{cases}$$

inevitably produces a reaction to the effect that 'this is not one function, but two', and much effort has to be expended in order to persuade the student that here indeed are not two functions but one, on the strength of the very same definition of function that he has firmly learnt off by heart in the secondary school. When you first acquaint the students with Dirichlet's function (which, it is worth pointing out, could well be shown to secondary school pupils) you meet the unchanging question, 'but what actually is the function?', 'how is it written down?'; if you suggest writing it thus: $y = \phi(x)$, then the student asks in upset tones, 'but is that really a formula?'—he is genuinely convinced that you are trying to trick him, and it becomes necessary to give a full hour's lecture, with historical excursions, to make him understand the simple fact, which should have been taught to him long ago in the

secondary school, that the formula $y = \phi(x)$ for Dirichlet's function
in no way differs in principle from the formula $y = \sin x$ used to
denote the sine curve; that there do not exist functions which in
principle cannot be described by formulae, and that the question of
depicting the formula has, as regards the idea of functional dependence,
only an outer, secondary significance.

But can and should the secondary schools give their pupils a picture
of functional dependence such as would correspond fully to modern
scientific ideas? In order to answer this question we must start out
from that basic principle which we consider an unswerving guide in
answering all questions of a similar type: in those cases where the
modern, scientific picture is too complicated for it to be understood by
schoolchildren, it can be replaced by a different, simplified picture, but
one which necessarily points in the same direction, *so that later on the
higher schools can develop this picture without having to throw out any
part of it as being unscientific.* This is just how the matter stands with
the concept of irrational number, and with the concept of limit. But
the schools must never, under any circumstances, replace the concept
as it is used in modern science by another which stands in contradiction
to it, so that the higher schools have to waste time and effort in un-
teaching the ideas that the students brought with them from the
secondary schools.

As far as the concept of functional dependence is concerned, we
would insist that the secondary schools can and must impart to their
students strictly scientific ideas and habits, not only in form but in
real content. The schools *can* do this because the modern scientific
concept of a function is simple, unburdened by any sort of formalism;
the lapses into a formalistic approach which we observe on every side
are not at all explained by the great simplicity of this approach, but
simply by the inadequate scientific standard and methodological
inertia of the text-book writers and a certain section of the methodologists and teachers. The schools must do this because, first, the fight
against formalism in basic mathematical concepts is a problem for the
Soviet schools which cannot be put off, and because, second, it is only
in this way that the higher schools can be spared the sad necessity of
persuading their students that the ideas they have brought with them
from the secondary schools conflict with modern scientific opinion and
must be got rid of at the shortest possible notice.

IV

We must now pass to the last and, in practice, most important question;
what should be changed in the traditional teaching of the subject of
functional dependence in order to overcome the defects discussed in

the preceding paragraph, and how should these changes be carried out?

The preparatory training in functional thinking, whose basic outline and style we attempted to describe earlier, makes it quite possible to introduce a fully scientific definition of functions of not only one but several variables in the topic 'functions and their graphs'. However, the traditional type of example considered immediately after this definition is quite capable of destroying any positive effect of the definition itself, and of giving the pupils the impression that the formal definition stands alone, so that in practice a function is simply a formula, and conversely a formula is a function. To avoid this, we consider it essential that even among the very first examples of functional dependence, along with the traditional algebraical and geometrical relations, some relations should be considered such as the Dirichlet function, or functions of the following type:

$$f(x) = \begin{cases} x^2, \text{ for } x \neq 0; \\ 1 \quad \text{ for } x = 0; \end{cases}$$

$$f(x) = \begin{cases} x, \text{ for } x = 1; \\ x^2, \text{ for } x \neq 1. \end{cases}$$

It is also very useful to consider such functions as $[x]$ (the greatest whole number not exceeding x), $x - [x]$, etc. In all cases, of course, a graphical illustration is necessary (and for Dirichlet's function and similar examples, some explanation of why it is hard to give a graphical illustration).

Here are some further examples of problems that we would consider useful subjects for classroom discussion:

(1) Give an analytical expression over the interval $-1 \leq x \leq 1$ for the function illustrated in the following diagram:

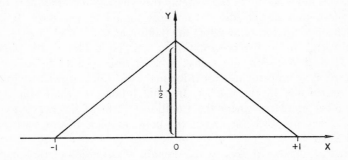

(2) A heavy point falls to the ground from a height of 1 metre; after falling, it remains lying at the point of impact; supposing that it starts to fall at time $t = 0$ sec. and that the acceleration due to gravity is $g = 9\cdot8$ m/sec^2, find an analytical expression for, and draw, the graph

of the dependence between the height of the point above ground, and time, for $0 \le t \le 1$ sec.

Every teacher will be able to think up for himself any number of similar examples.

It is very desirable that the pupils should be told about the meaning and role of an analytical expression as an agreed notation for a frequently used function, drawing a parallel between the notation for a function using a formula and the notation for a number using figures: just as figures do not give rise to the number but serve only as its outer image, so the formula expressing some function does not give rise to it, but serves only as an apparatus for describing it. And just as history knows a whole series of different methods for writing down the unchanging numbers, so the analytical expression for a given function is a historical phenomenon, having its own beginning and evolutionary path. If, for example, we were to agree today that we would write $\psi(x)$ for Dirichlet's function, and if this agreement were to be upheld on a world-wide basis, and enter into familiar usage, then after a certain time $\psi(x)$ would become just such an 'analytical expression', just such a 'formula', as $\sqrt{x}$ or lg x, and whoever wrote $\psi(x)$ would not have to explain in words the meaning of this notation, any more than it is necessary to explain each time in words what is meant by $\sqrt{x}$ or lg x. We suggest that a discussion of this question would greatly strengthen the pupils' understanding of the most important, fundamental idea that the function is the primary reality, whereas the analytical expression is only a tool created for studying functions; that the function exists and can be studied without the aid of the analytical expression.

This basic thought should be emphasized in all subsequent teaching. Here it is not a matter of breaking up the syllabus—nothing more than the most insignificant editorial changes should be necessary. It is a matter of scrupulously avoiding anything that might lead, and in fact would lead, to a misrepresentation of this basic idea in the pupils' minds. Such occasions are many; in most cases, the initial source of the error is an unfortunate exposition in the text-book, which is followed too uncritically by the teacher. In what follows we shall indicate a a number of places where the traditional form of the exposition is particularly unsatisfactory from the point of view of our particular problem.

First of all, this applies to the domain of definition or (less happy phrase) 'region of existence' of a function. The well-known text-book tradition (including text-books for the higher schools) is to work out this domain from the formula; it is said, for example, that 'the function $+ \sqrt{1 - x^2}$ exists only for $|x| \le 1$'. Such terminology must be considered mathematically imprecise and pedagogically dangerous, for at its base lies the thought that the function defined for $|x| \leq 1$ by the formula $+ \sqrt{1 - x^2}$ cannot be defined outside this interval; that the existence of the function comes to an end where the analytical expression used to describe it ceases to make sense. From there, of course, it is not far to the usual objection that conditions of the form

$$y = \begin{cases} + \sqrt{1 - x^2} & \text{for } |x| \leq 1 \\ x^2 - 1 & \text{for } |x| > 1 \end{cases}$$

define 'not one function but two', for if the function $+ \sqrt{1 - x^2}$ does not exist for $|x| \leq 1$, then evidently our definition of the quantity y beyond the bounds of the interval $-1 \leq x \leq 1$ must represent a new, 'second', function.

In fact, of course, the situation is as follows: the formula (and not the function) $+ \sqrt{1 - x^2}$ is by existing agreement capable of representing the given function only for $|x| \leq 1$; hence, if we wish to represent the given function beyond this interval, we must find for this purpose a further analytical expression; the expression $+ \sqrt{1 - x^2}$ itself loses any meaning for $|x| > 1$ (it goes without saying that here we are considering only real values of the function). This state of affairs is so straightforward and elementary that there should be no difficulty in getting the pupils to understand it. In a completely analogous fashion, the thought can be planted in their minds that the symbol $y = \lg x$ makes sense (and therefore can be used in the definition of some function) only for $x > 0$, etc. Along with these remarks it would be useful to point out that

$$y = \begin{cases} \lg x & \text{for } x > 0 \\ x & \text{for } x \leq 0 \end{cases}$$

is a genuine, fully-fledged function, and to illustrate this function by its graph.

In connection with the domains of definition of a function, we would also like to remark that it is desirable to make that general principle plain to the pupils whereby a function is, as a rule, defined for those values of the argument which have a real meaning in the given problem. Thus, for example, p_n, the perimeter of a right n-gon inscribed to a circle of radius 1, is effectively meaningful only for $n \geq 3$; the number of permutations of n elements is meaningful for all natural numbers n; if the argument T denotes temperature, then in most cases there is no point in defining the function for $T \leq -273°C$, etc. In general, the vital point in choosing the domain of definition of the function should be the real significance of the functional relation being studied, and not the formal analytical expression employed in this or that part of this region.

Finally, we must pause over a concept where the formal approach finds its clearest expression, and where, therefore, there are particularly great dangers from the point of view we have been considering. This is the concept of a 'many-valued' function, first met by the pupils in the extraction of roots, and later in the study of inverse trigonometrical functions. The concept of a many-valued function belongs wholly to that epoch when the analytical expression was not a tool of investigation but the progenitor of functional relations. As matters stand, it is just as if, in a country fully won over to the new, real understanding of this concept, there stood one enemy fortress, besieged on every side, but until now not laying down its arms. This fortress is the concept of the many-valued function, and the battle against it on the school front is made all the more difficult because not only the higher schools, but even mathematical science itself, cannot yet rid themselves of this concept, although it stands in explicit conceptual and stylistic contradiction to the whole spirit of the modern theory of functional relations.

What, in fact, is a many-valued function? We are told: y is a many-valued function of x if to every value of x there correspond several values of y. But what is this 'several'? If it means a definite, finite number, then the definition is insufficient even for the needs of the secondary schools, with their infinitely-many-valued arcsin. But if the word 'several' has an unspecified numerical meaning, and can include where necessary even the value 'infinity', then evidently *every* quantity y is a function of *any* quantity x, so that no matter what x and y may mean, for each value of x the quantity y will take at least some values from all the possible values it can have; in this way the whole meaning of the concept of functional dependence is lost.

Every such attempt to explain the definition in detail, to pin it down to this or that stipulation, leads to complications that on the one hand are quite unnecessary, and on the other certainly beyond the grasp of a schoolchild.

Modern mathematics in its higher branches makes use of a whole series of extensions of the idea of a function. It by no means refuses to consider the case where the argument is a number and the value of the function some set of numbers. However, this has nothing in common with the needs not only of the secondary schools but even of the basic course in analysis at the higher schools, at least as regards the theory of a real variable. Quite a different breeze has blown the idea of many-valuedness into these elementary regions. Two hundred years ago, our forefathers, in the study of inverse functions, adopted the custom of writing in a single formula $y = \sqrt{x}$ both solutions of the equation $y^2 = x$, and in the single formula $y = \text{Arcsin } x$ the whole infinite set of solutions of the equation $\sin y = x$. But this was the epoch when 'a single formula' meant 'a single function'. And when, later on, the whole scientific world took up a new, true definition of the concept of a function, and it became clear that the functions '$\sqrt{x}$' or 'Arcsin x' did not suit this definition, the term 'many-valued function' was thought up to save the situation.[1]

In actual fact the concept of a many-valued function is quite redundant for the elementary theory of functions of a real variable. Pedagogically, it is dangerous (in the higher schools as much as in the secondary schools) because (1) in style and spirit it is a continuation of the formalistic point of view which has been outgrown and rejected by modern science; (2) it introduces unnecessary complications into the definition of a function, overburdening it to such an extent that it fully loses its meaning. As in many other cases, the situation in fact is so simple that there is no difficulty in bringing it within the pupils' grasp, without making any mention of many-valued functions; it is only necessary to resolve to throw off the yoke of tradition, which has been holding up this point in the study of elementary functions for many centuries. After writing down and investigating the relation $y^2 = x$, we convince ourselves that both functions $y = + \sqrt{x}$ and $y = - \sqrt{x}$ satisfy this relation for all $x \geq 0$, or, if it is convenient to write *one formula* for *both* these functions, then we write $y = \pm \sqrt{x}$ or $y = e \sqrt{x}$, where e is a parameter which can take the two values $+ 1$ and $- 1$. That is all. Similarly, in discussing the relation $\sin y = x$, we arrive at the conclusion that each of the functions

$$y = (- 1)^n \arcsin x + n, \qquad \dots\dots\dots\dots\dots\dots(1)$$

where n is an arbitrary integer, and arcsin x is the well-known 'principal value', satisfies this relation; in other words, the sine has not one but an infinite set of inverse functions, one such function corresponding to each value of n in the formula (1). Finally, it is not even necessary to object to the symbol $y = $ Arcsin x as an abbreviation for the expression (1); it is only necessary to point out clearly that here the symbol Arcsin x denotes not one function but a whole set of functions, and that the structure of this set is very much more clearly displayed in the notation (1). That is all. Such a system of exposition retains the simplicity and clarity which characterize the modern definition of the concept of functional dependence; function and formula are kept clearly distinct from each other, and there is no room for unnecessary complications that obscure the very sense of the concept of function. At the same time, this method of exposition contains nothing more complicated than is contained in the traditional exposition, using 'many-valued functions', that has taken root in our text-books and teaching practice.

[1] Of course, the situation has been somewhat schematized in our discussion, and in fact the growth of the theory of functions of a complex variable has also played a considerable role in the process described; however, this in no way affects our pedagogical conclusions.

MATHEMATICAL DEFINITIONS IN THE SECONDARY SCHOOLS [1]

Questions as to the character, problems, and peculiarities of definitions in the school mathematics course are raised at every turn for particular concrete issues, and are frequently debated in our methodological press. This is understandable and natural; on the one hand, every teacher knows from experience just how much importance a well-constructed definition may have in forming a proper scientific outlook; and on the other hand, one and the same concept may be defined in entirely different ways in different text-books and teaching manuals. It is easy to understand how questions as to which of the suggested definitions is scientifically best-formed, or which is methodologically most effective, disturb the teacher, arouse his interests as a scientist and methodologist, set him looking for explanations, and often provoke him into putting forward (and sometimes even to propagandizing insistently) his own point of view.

It is absolutely clear that none of the questions arising from particular concrete issues can be satisfactorily solved until we leave off fruitless quarrelling over the definition of particular concepts, turn to a general statement of this important scientific and methodological problem, and work out the basic principles for giving mathematical definitions in the schools. Until this is done, any discussion on no matter what particular concept will remain fruitless. Indeed, can it really be possible to select the most appropriate definition of this or that concept if we do not know what properties or particular features of the chosen definition will cause us to prefer it to the others? Surely this would be as if two judges started quarrelling over the correct decision without knowing the law of the country.

Even a cursory acquaintance with the character of the inquiries and opinions put forward by teachers with regard to particular mathematical definitions shows quite convincingly that, so far as the main questions of principle are concerned, there is such a disparity of opinions and points of view that we would have no hope of reaching agreement on any concrete issue; any discussion will remain fruitless so long as the debators start off from opposing basic principles. If one teacher con-

[1] First published in Matematika v Shkole (1941 No. 1) under the title 'O matematiche-skikh Opredelenyakh v svedney shkole.'

siders the crucial test for an effective definition to be its accordance with modern scientific ideas, another its closeness to practice, a third its immediate ease of comprehension, a fourth its generality, a fifth its similarity to the definitions of analogous concepts, and so on, then of course we cannot expect any agreement in choosing the most appropriate definition.

But the study of teachers' comments leads one to even more far-reaching conclusions. It shows quite definitely that the question of the nature of a definition, of what is meant by *defining* a concept, is not fully clear. Here various confusions hold sway: a full-valued scientific definition is often replaced by a description owing nothing to anyone, or simply by an indication of the role and significance of the 'defined' concept in this or that practical application ('a number is the result of a calculation or a measurement'). It very often happens that of two competing 'definitions' one indeed defines the concept, while the other has no pretensions to such a role, being merely a modest explanatory description; clearly, no two such 'definitions' can ever compete, for the problems that they set themselves are completely different; and yet how often with us, in just such cases, people take up arms to prove the superiority of one 'definition' over the others.

It is very clear that before choosing the most effective system of definitions, before even setting out the general principles on which such a choice should be made, we must come to a proper understanding as to what is meant by a mathematical definition. It is necessary to set up absolutely precise characteristics that will distinguish a definition from a more or less complete description, to investigate as clearly as possible the roles of definitions and descriptions in school teaching, and to clarify what methodological consequences are entailed by the logical difference between concepts that are truly defined and concepts in whose introduction we limit ourselves to a description.

It is precisely to this preliminary aim that the present small article is devoted.

Definitions in Mathematical Science

In the 1938 edition of A. P. Kiselev's 'Arithmetic'[1], subtraction was defined as an operation which consisted in taking away from one number however many units were contained in the other number. In the earlier editions of the same course, subtraction was defined as an operation which consisted in seeking the second member of a summation given the sum and the first member. This alteration gave rise to a lively discussion among the methodologists and teaching staff, and in particular, very many found A. P. Kiselev's alteration to be in-

---

[1] A. P. Kiselev's book was the standard text up to the Great World War (B.G.).

C

appropriate and put forward the view that the original definition should have been retained. The motivation, when such was given, took varied forms, but most frequently the supporters of the old definition pointed out the desirability of retaining the analogue with the definition of division (seeking the second term in a product from the product and the first term); conversely, those upholding the new definition maintained that here was an analogy with the definition of addition. Not once in this discussion, however, was it pointed out that the controversy was not between two logically equivalent pretendents. Whereas the earlier editions contained a true scientific definition (for here the concept of subtraction was reduced to already known, earlier defined concepts sum, member of sum), the change introduced in the 1938 edition represented a complete, basic refusal to make *any* definition of the concept of subtraction, and a replacement of the definition by an explanatory phrase. When you say 'to subtract is to take away' this represents a substitution of the term 'to take away' for the term 'to subtract', which, perhaps, sounds somewhat less forbidding to the mathematically inexperienced ear but is evidently no easier to define logically than the term 'to subtract.' Thus, in the 1938 edition, the author quite consciously accepts the view that it is inappropriate to give the schoolchildren any definition of subtraction, and recommends that in the introduction of this concept we should limit ourselves to a simple explanatory phrase not pretending to any defining value (as indeed was done for the operation of *addition* in all the preceding editions). At the present moment, the question of how far this innovation is methodologically justified need not concern us; for our purposes it is important only to establish that in the discussion arising from this issue the alternatives themselves were most often incorrectly stated: it should not have been a question of a choice between two competing definitions, but of whether in the elementary school course the concept of subtraction is better introduced through a definition, or through an explanatory description making use of familiar terms. Had such a correct statement of the problem been made, it would most certainly have led to a significant increase in the productivity of the discussion.

In teachers' letters, the 'definition' of addition is also often the subject of sharp criticism; in analyzing this 'definition', the authors of these letters point out that it is tautologous and in fact defines nothing; some of these comrades recommend altogether dispensing with any attempts to define addition and taking it as an initial, undefined concept. To all these critics the answer must be made that their excitement and sarcasm serve only to break down a door that is already open. All their critical remarks are quite correct, but the fact is that the standard text (and for that matter any course of elementary arithmetic) has never tried to define the concept of addition; in relation to the pupils' ages this would be a quite hopeless problem, as is clear to any methodologist. What these critics take for a definition, and, as such, subject to severe criticism, is in fact, according to the author's intentions, a mere unpretentious description, having the aim of making the new concept easier to master; it can be rated successful or unsuccessful from the methodological point of view, but there is no sense in analyzing or criticising its logical value, for it does not pretend to have any value of this type.

We have given these examples in order to indicate how easily an inadequate understanding of the fundamental characteristics and peculiarities of mathematical definitions may lead to futile and groundless (and thereby unproductive) discussions. By no means every phrase uttered in the attempt to clarify the meaning of a newly introduced concept need pretend to the role of a definition of that concept, and ignorance of this truth often serves as the source of futile arguments.

The only formulations of a new concept that can serve as definitions of that concept (and which in fact are accepted as definitions in mathematics) *are those which fully reduce the new concept to concepts already familiar in the given scientific field.* When we say that a prime number is a number having only two divisors, then that is a definition, for here the new concept is completely referred back to concepts that have, in this particular scientific field, been introduced at an earlier stage. Similarly, when we say that division consists of seeking one of the terms in a product, given the product and the other term, then we are giving a full definition of the corresponding arithmetical operation.

If, however, in order to clarify the introduction of a new concept, we base it fully, or even partially, on considerations taken from practical life, from other sciences, or from everyday experience, and not on concepts already established in the same scientific field, then that is an explanatory description, and for all its pedagogical value cannot be called a definition. When we say that an angle is a measure of the mutual inclination of two straight lines, then that is a very valuable explanation from the pedagogical point of view, but of course it is no sort of definition, because the term 'inclination', to which we wish to reduce the new concept, is nowhere and in no way defined in the preceding discussion. When we say that 'a number is the result of a calculation or a measurement', then this phrase describes very well the main applications of the concept of a number in practical life, but of course it cannot be taken as a definition of the concept of number because calculation and measurement cannot be considered arithmetical concepts defined and introduced before the concept of number.

In the development and exposition of any branch of mathematical (and strictly speaking any other) science we make the rigorous demand that every new concept should be defined in the exact sense indicated above. By its very essence, mathematical science cannot work with concepts that have not been given such a definition. This situation leads, as is well-known, to one characteristic difficulty. Any science has its beginning, its *primary*, basic concepts, with whose introduction its exposition begins. How can these concepts be defined, if by a definition we mean a reduction to concepts that have already been introduced in the given scientific field?

Suppose that we are setting up an exposition of geometry, and that as the primary simplest concept we choose the concept of a point—the simplest geometrical form. Can we define this concept? Evidently, we cannot, since this is the *first* concept in the given science, there are no preceding concepts, and therefore we can find no way of reducing this concept to earlier concepts. It is quite clear that inevitably we shall be faced with a similar state of affairs in setting up any branch of mathematical science.

It is well-known how modern mathematics finds a way out of this difficulty. At the beginning of every scientific field a small group of primary, undefined concepts is introduced. It is pointed out explicitly that these primary concepts cannot be and must not be defined, and at the same time the categorical demand is made that, after listing these primary, undefined concepts, every new concept introduced at a later stage must be given an exact definition, i.e. a full reduction either to the primary concepts or to other concepts that have already been defined.

However, even if the primary concepts are not defined, this does not mean that nothing needs to be done apart from naming them. Between these primary concepts regular, universally valid, mutual interrelations are set up. The list of these mutual relations must be set out in full when the primary concepts are introduced; these mutual relations among the primary concepts make up the axioms, or the primary, unproved truths of the given scientific field. Just as, after setting up the list of primary concepts, every new concept had to be exactly defined, so after setting up the list of axioms every new assertion must be given an exact *proof*, i.e. a logical reduction to the axioms or to assertions that have already been proved. Thus, *the primary concepts are not defined, but listed together with the formal relations which hold between them and constitute the axioms of the given scientific field.* To clarify this statement, let us take as an example one of the most widely accepted systems of primary elements for the arithmetic of the natural numbers (the Peano system).[1]

[1]Peano (1858–1932)—an Italian mathematician; his system of axioms was put forward in 1889. (B.G.).

Primary Concepts

1. Number (natural).
2. Unity.
3. Successor.

Axioms

1. Unity is a number.
2. Every number has a unique successor.
3. Unity is not a successor for any number.
4. (The principle of complete induction). If any assertion is true for unity and if, whenever it is true for some particular number, it is also true for the successor of that number, then that assertion is true for any number.

The development of mathematics has shown that on the basis of this collection of primary concepts and primary truths it is really possible to build up the whole edifice of arithmetic; all new concepts (in particular, the arithmetical operations) can be precisely defined, all assertions (in particular, all the laws of the arithmetical operations) can be rigorously proved (i.e. become theorems).

For us, what is important from this discussion is the following point, not usually emphasized enough in accounts of the axiomatic method: *at the base of every mathematical discipline lie certain primary concepts, which are not defined, although at the very beginning a list is given of the mutual relations which hold between them; this list makes up the system of axioms for the given scientific field; once the primary concepts have been listed, all new concepts must be capable of exact definition.*

Let us make one final remark. In the system of primary concepts of geometry suggested by Hilbert, and widely accepted in contemporary mathematics, the point, straight line, and plane are taken as being primary concepts. However, there are a large number of other systems of primary concepts for geometry, suggested by different authors, in which quite other concepts are accepted as primary. If, say, the plane was absent from the list of primary concepts of one of these other systems, then in that system the plane would no longer be a primary concept and so would be subject to definition. In general the list of primary concepts of the given scientific field is far from being uniquely defined by the subject-matter of that field; from the formal point of view it can be chosen arbitrarily in accordance with this or that particular system of exposition. A concept which in one exposition might be a primary concept, and therefore undefined, in a different system might be subject to and capable of definition. In this way, the definability or undefinability of a concept is not an objective property of the concept, arising from its content, but depends critically on the chosen system of exposition.

On the introduction of new concepts in the school mathematics course

If, as we have seen, science itself is in principle not in a position to define all its concepts, then it is quite evident that no such demand can be made of the school course. No matter how we might construct that course, provided only that we do not wish to deceive our pupils, we should have to leave undefined some of the concepts that we introduced. This should be made a starting point and an immediate factor of all further investigations into the problem we have been discussing.

At the same time we see that the basic questions facing school teaching after this factor has been taken into account may be summarized as follows:

1. Which concepts in the school mathematics course should be defined and which should be left undefined? (We saw that this question admits several answers even within the bounds of mathematics itself.)

2. When we refrain from defining some particular concept, how, with what sort of explanatory phrases, should this definition be replaced in the process of teaching?

3. Is it appropriate to draw the pupils' attention to the difference between definitions and descriptions of concepts, and if so, to what extent and by what means?

We proceed now to a brief consideration of these three questions.

As we saw above, an inescapable requirement in the logical construction of any mathematical discipline is the reduction of the number of undefined concepts (and the number of axioms) to a minimum. This means that none of the primary concepts should be capable of being defined, or in other words, that every concept that can be defined must be defined, and ought not to be listed among the undefined concepts.

Can we and ought we to uphold this requirement in constructing the school course? We would suggest that there can be no two opinions on this question, for if we desired, for example, to define all concepts in the arithmetic classes for forms IV–V, we should have to define addition and multiplication by the method of complete induction (and also, let us note in passing, to prove their properties) to children 11 or 12 years old. In practice, the axiomatic construction of any scientific field, being historically always the final and never the initial stage in the development of the given field, is beyond the range, not only of school children, but of higher school students in their first years of study; it demands a level of formal logical culture that would be at best within the range of a university student graduating in mathematics.

Thus there can be no doubt that the number of mathematical concepts introduced without definition in the school course must be considerably larger than in a formal development of the given discipline. For example, it is clear that the concept of sum (of two natural numbers), which is usually a defined concept in the formal development of arithmetic, cannot be defined within the bounds of the school course. By what indications should we judge whether some particular concept should be given a definition within the bounds of the school course? To give the discussion of this question a more concrete form, we shall carry it through in terms of a suitable example.

We saw above that the concept of subtraction was considered by some methodologists to be better defined (by reducing it to the concepts of sum and members of a sum introduced at an earlier stage) while others considered it to be better left without definition (as was made clear above, phrases such as 'to subtract is to take away' and their like cannot be considered in any way a definition of the operation of subtraction). This question is indeed controversial; we do not propose to solve it here, but only to consider the various arguments that have been put forward by representatives of the two points of view.

Those who insist on a definition of subtraction argue roughly as follows:

1. The definition of the concept of subtraction is simple enough for it to be mastered without difficulty by pupils of classes IV–V.

2. By defining subtraction in terms of addition we establish an immediate mutual connection between these two concepts—a connection which in some other approach could only be brought out through special efforts.

3. Since division is usually defined in terms of multiplication, and since the connection between addition and subtraction has the same formal characteristics as the connection between multiplication and division, it would be methodologically inconsistent to treat subtraction differently from division.

All three arguments listed are well grounded. On the other hand, the often-heard argument which runs on roughly the following lines: 'by defining subtraction in terms of addition we are reducing it to concepts that are already familiar; but by defining subtraction as a 'taking away' we reduce it to a concept that is just as new as subtraction itself and has nowhere previously been defined' must be considered erroneous. To say nothing of the fact that here, for the second 'definition', we have a simple explanatory phrase, which of course nobody would ever think of using as a definition, such an argument sets out from the clearly unacceptable thesis that the conflict between definition and description must always be decided in favour of the definition, provided only that such a definition is possible. By arguing in this way, we would have to admit that there were equal grounds for defining addition too, and indeed for defining any concept at all that was not listed among the primary concepts in a formal, logical account of the given discipline.

On the other side, the representatives of the opposite point of view make the following points:

1. The real process that is reflected in arithmetic through the concept of subtraction is so familiar to the child from his every-day experience, that it would be pedagogically unsatisfactory to acquaint him with this concept in a form cut off from its real roots.

2. A fully effective method of introducing subtraction, based on the real process corresponding to it, can be carried through by establishing the equivalence of the terms 'to subtract', and 'to take away', the latter term being well familiar to the children from their every-day life.

3. What is here suggested cannot, of course be considered a definition of subtraction; however, the number of concepts that must be introduced in the school course without definition is so large that to increase or decrease this number by one can hardly make any significant difference.

4. As far as the connection between addition and subtraction is concerned, there is no doubt that this should be fully established only after the pupils have already become familiar with subtraction on the basis of examples and descriptive explanations.

We must admit that these arguments too are genuinely convincing. As was mentioned earlier, it forms no part of our task to solve this debate: we wish to extract from the example considered only those general motives that in particular cases may cause us, when first introducing some new concept, to prefer a definition to a description, or vice versa. The most important of these are as follows:

1. In introducing each new concept, it is first of all necessary to investigate whether it admits a definition in terms of concepts introduced at an earlier stage. If it is given that no such definition can exist, then, of course, we must accept the given concept as a primary concept (undefined), refuse to make any attempt to define it, and seek appropriate pedagogical alternatives to the definition in the shape of explanatory phrases.

2. If the definition of the new concept is logically possible, then it is in order to consider the question, to what extent is it within reach from the pedagogical point of view—that is to say, is it within the pupils' range at the given age? It will readily be understood that this assessment should be made on the basis not of the formal but the intrinsic content of the new concept; the question is not whether the pupils are capable of formally learning off by heart and remembering the given definition, but to what extent, at the given age, is the logical formulation capable of leading to a proper understanding of the concept—its real nature, its connections with other concepts, with life, with practice. If the definition (on account of its extreme abstractness, exceptional com-

plexity or for other reasons) is such that nothing can be expected from it in this respect, then this is always an argument in favour of rejecting the given definition and replacing it by some pedagogical equivalent.

3. If, as often happens, the object or image of the new mathematical concept is already well-known to the pupils from their everyday experience (addition, subtraction, angle, straight line, circle) then this is always an argument in favour of appealing to just these connections with reality, rather than to a formal definition, when the concept is first introduced.

4. On the contrary, if in the given scientific field a fundamental role is played by the new concept's logical connections with concepts defined at an earlier stage, and if the formal definition of the new concept reveals these connections with sufficient clarity and simplicity, then this is a reason for giving a formal logical definition of the new concept even at its first introduction.

5. In cases where we have two or more parallel groups of concepts, whose formal connections show a significant analogy (addition and subtraction, multiplication and division) it is desirable in the aims of elegance and systematic exposition to adopt an identical approach to both groups of concepts—i.e. either in both cases build the exposition up on formal definitions, or in both cases refrain from such definitions.

6. We should point out that a formal definition and an explanatory description appealing to real connections and visual images do not, generally speaking, exclude one another; on the contrary, in those cases where the concept is introduced on the basis of a formal definition, we are (generally speaking) not freed from the obligation to point out as soon as possible after setting up the definition, the concept's real significance, to discuss all aspects of its visual forms, and describe those moments in real life and practical activity whose abstract reflection it is called upon to represent. In many cases it is only a question of which should precede, a formal definition or a visual and practical description. It should not be thought, however, that this consideration can deprive the problem of its real pedagogical significance: we know how sometimes it is just the character and circumstances of the *first acquaintance* with the concept that has the decisive influence. Even in adult years, in recalling this or that term, associations rise to the surface which are connected with this character of the first acquaintance. As a rule, the whole style and effectiveness, as well as the practical success, of the concept, depend vitally on the circumstances surrounding its first entry into our consciousness.

Let us turn now to the question of how to introduce in the school course concepts which for logical or pedagogical reasons cannot be formally defined. It is clear first of all that in this respect school teaching cannot follow the same path as mathematical science. As we have seen, in mathematical science, when the primary (undefined) concepts are introduced, an equivalent to a definition is made up by noting all the mutual relations which hold among these initial concepts, and setting them out in the form of a list of axioms. But this basic function of the axioms undoubtedly represents one of the most difficult points to grasp for anyone making a first acquaintance with the axiomatic method of providing a logical foundation for mathematical disciplines. Nor can there be any talk of attempting to make any moves in this direction within the bounds of the school course; the most we could desire in relation to the school course is that the role of a definition and the role of an axiom, taken in isolation, should enter clearly into the pupils' understanding. However, because of its logical complexity, the situation where an axiom can serve in place of a definition passes beyond the bounds of what is possible in the school course.

Where the new concept is for some reason introduced without a definition, it is quite clear that for school teaching purposes, we must seek not a formal but a pedagogical equivalent to the unsatisfactory definition. It is not the formal links of the new concept with other concepts which must provide the material for those explanatory descriptions that are to replace the definition, but their real connections; and not only their connections with other concepts, but also their connections with real-life objects and occasions.

It is clear that the concept of a natural number cannot be defined in the elementary arithmetic course. Indeed, we never define it. But we say that a number is a unit or a collection of units, and this forms a good explanatory description because it links the concept of a number with the concept of units (also, of course, undefined) through a term as familiar to any child in his everyday life as that of a 'collection'. We say also that a number is the result of a calculation—again a good explanatory phrase; although there is no word in it as to the essence of a number, it directly points out to the child that familiar, everyday, practical operation whose mature fruit is always a number. Such explanatory descriptions have, of course, considerable pedagogical effect. They at once allow the new concept to take its proper place alongside other concepts in the pupil's mind, and accustom him to associate this concept with those images, objects and phenomena of real life in which in fact it is rooted.

The concept of an angle clearly cannot be defined in elementary geometry. And thus in place of a definition we give an explanatory reference: 'An angle is a measure of the mutual inclination of two straight lines'. What is an inclination and what is a measure are questions which up to this time have never been formally considered in the course, but in spite of this our reference undoubtedly has considerable pedagogical value: it simultaneously links the concept of angle with a clear visual image, and describes one of the most important practical functions of this concept—a function whose value is well within the grasp of a child's understanding. We say also that an angle is the part of a plane contained within two half-lines having a common origin. This new explanatory description also associates the concept of angle with a simple visual image, in this case underlining a different aspect, a different peculiarity of the new concept: every angle divides the points of a plane into two parts, those lying inside the angle, and those lying outside it.

The examples we have taken teach us the following. Explanatory descriptions that are called upon to replace the definition of a new concept must always appeal to something that has already a firm place in the pupil's mind. This could be either a concept from the same scientific field that has already been securely and actively assimilated, or some phenomena or practical activities that are familiar to him from everyday experience. In setting up these or other links between the new concept and such firmly mastered ingredients of the child's consciousness, we shall, without pretending to give a logical basis for the new concept, ensure that in the future, when recalling this concept, the correct associations will be called up in his mind, helping him to operate with it without error. Understandably, this role of explanatory descriptions makes them an exceptionally important aspect of teaching. An explanatory description need not, of course, reveal the sense of the new concept in full detail (otherwise it would be a definition); it may limit itself to an indication of certain aspects of this sense, although we must take every precaution to avoid the state of affairs where, in the hope of making the description easier to understand, the sense of the concept is distorted by the explanatory description. Such a distortion, however harmless it may seem, will in the sequel lead inevitably to actual logical errors. It is sufficient to recall the harm, so hard to repair, that is caused by the (regrettably rather widespread) simplifications in the treatment of the basic concepts of infinitesimal analysis.

It remains for us to consider the question of to what extent the logical difference between definitions and explanatory descriptions should find a counterpart in methodological differences between the treatment of these two approaches to the introduction of new concepts, and in what these differences should consist. We are inclined to give this question a high significance, since, according to our ideas, no small number of errors and injuries are committed in this respect.

In teachers' letters we very often meet with questions similar to the following: 'Which definition of an angle is correct—as the measure of the inclination etc., or as the part of the plane, etc.?' 'Which definition of a number is the more scientific—as the result of a calculation or measurement, or as that property of a set which remains after the removal of the nature and ordering of its elements?' The mass of questions of this kind, while affording gratifying evidence of the presence among our teachers of a lively interest in mathematical definition as a problem of methodology, at the same time shows quite clearly that in many cases the teachers themselves are not yet fully clear as to how this problem should be stated.

The questions that we have set down above, and all those similar to them, are of course based on a misunderstanding. First of all, not one of the competing 'definitions', as they are termed by the questioners, is really a definition; they are all explanatory descriptions, having as their aim to uncover this or that aspect of the new concept. From this it follows that if either one of them is 'correct', or 'scientific' (i.e. does not distort the sense of the concept), then it is by no means necessary that the other is any 'less correct' or 'less scientific'. They in no way contradict each other, but to the contrary, as we saw above, supplement each other in a most useful fashion.

Of course, from this incorrect understanding of the logical situation follow also mistakes in methodology. From this source above all others stems the rather widespread tendency in our schools to set the children to learn 'definitions' by heart which in fact are not definitions at all. When we chanced to see forty written papers, each of which began with the question 'What is a ratio?' and followed up with the inevitable answer 'A ratio is the result of a comparison, etc.', we must confess that we took this as an insult to thinking man in his childhood years, for the asserted 'definition' is of course no sort of a definition, but only a burdensome, wordy attempt at an explanatory phrase which, to learn by heart, is an obvious mistake.

Not long ago Professor S. A. Yanovskaya told us of one young man, a good pupil, who was upset because his marks had been reduced when he was unable to answer the question 'What is a fraction?' This young man said in upset tones, 'I understand why we have to know how to multiply and divide fractions, but tell me, where do we use the definition of a fraction?' We are bound to confess that we are wholly on the side of the young man, for any 'definition' of a fraction that can be given in the elementary arithmetic course can be at best a useful explanatory phrase. If the pupil made use of this description in order to master better and more quickly the apparatus of fractions, then that is all we can ask of him. The demand that the pupils should learn this description off by heart can only be described as a methodological absurdity.

When we require that definitions should sometimes be learnt by the pupils in full, this has its sound methodological basis. A logical definition is a formula from which nothing can be dropped and to which not a word can be added, or otherwise the sense will be distorted. In demanding that the pupils learn such definitions by heart we are therefore instilling in them just that scrupulous attitude towards a definition which, by its logical nature, the definition deserves. It is useful, we would suggest, to show even schoolchildren how quickly the sense of a definition is distorted if we change even so much as a single word; such examples would help the pupils to understand that the word-by-word memorization of a definition is an act of high logical culture and not a piece of scholastic cramming.

But what can be the sense in learning off by heart phrases that merely aim to clarify the new concept by appealing to familiar images? To say nothing of the fact that several such explanatory descriptions can be given for one and the same concept (and the more the better), and so by choosing one of them for word-by-word memorization we are leading the pupils to the erroneous conclusion that the explanation we have chosen is in some way logically different from the others, it is necessary to take into account that in any such explanatory description we can vary the text in a large number of ways without distorting the sense of the concept being described, and without diminishing the description's methodological effectiveness. It is absolutely clear that in these circumstances a word-by-word memorization of such an explanation would represent an unjustified fixation of a more or less arbitrary text. Such a fixation can and in fact does have a whole series of undesirable consequences. The most important of these is that the pupil's attention and effort is directed in the first place towards the formal aspects of the memorized explanation, whereas the logical nature and methodological purpose of the explanation are such that its formal side plays a quite subsidiary role. Moreover, in such a memorization, the real associations, the links with practical activities, are pushed into the background, although it was in these that lay the whole purpose of the explanation. If the pupil whom we mentioned earlier had made good use at the proper time of the explanation of a fraction given to him, if he had completely mastered the apparatus of fractions, was sensible of its real links and had understood its practical applications, then what purpose would we have in demanding from him a word-by-word memorization of one or other of the explanatory phrases given to him at an earlier stage? For you see this is no definition, in which every word has its irreplaceable logical weight, indispensible in all ensuing formal discussions. It is an unassuming explanatory description, of which we can never make use in any later formal discussions. Its role is played out once the given section has been mastered, and we must therefore regard its word-for-word memorization as a harmful scholastic stupidity, distorting the true state of affairs.

This detailed study of the special question of word-by-word memorization of definitions should make clear those methodological differences which must hold between the introduction of new concepts by means of definitions and by means of explanatory descriptions. In passing, let us add also, that we would consider it useful if, in order to avoid confusion, descriptions that were not definitions were left unemphasized in the text books and were not distinguished by any special script; also, where desirable, if the introduction of new concepts was accompanied by not one but several such explanations. It is quite unnecessary that the author of the text-book should have to choose between the phrases 'An angle is the measure of the inclination etc.' and 'An angle is the part of the plane, etc.'. Ideally he would use both pictures in explaining the new concept, in the appropriate contexts of course, and not to single out either as fundamental dogma.

Let us remark in conclusion that the scrupulous methodological discrimination between definitions and simple descriptions which we have recommended would have the further important effect that from their earliest years the pupils would be taught to treat definitions with the rigorous logical attention that they require, and not to lump together under the name of 'definitions' all the irresponsible phrases uttered when some new concept is introduced. In this way we would remove one of the greatest defects in logical culture that has spread in our time among the graduates of the secondary schools—a defect whose evil consequences sometimes endure throughout the whole period of a student's higher school education, and in particular cases even beyond its bounds.

Conclusion

The question of finding the most appropriate method of introducing this or the other new mathematical concept in the secondary school course is one of the most responsible problems of mathematical methodology. As we have mentioned already in the introduction to this article, before starting to discuss any particular concepts we should thoroughly elucidate the general principles which lie at the basis of all concrete problems in this field. But even before working out these principles it is necessary to reach exact agreement on the question of what is a mathematical definition, what is its role in the school course, how and by what should it be replaced where a logical definition is impossible or methodologically undesirable.

Our article has been devoted just to this last circle of questions. The problem of choosing the most effective method of introducing a concept has not been solved for a single concrete example, nor has it even been set up in any detail. But this was not our aim. We set ourselves only one task: to clarify as far as possible the background against which such questions should be posed and answered. Up till now we have seen much confusion, with disputants arguing in different languages, using the same terms with different meanings, understanding neither one another nor the remarks of a third person. In such circumstances discussion cannot be fruitful. In the present article we have gathered together a number of remarks which seem to us absolutely uncontroversial, perhaps even to some extent banal, whose sole aim is to set a more or less firm foundation for any future discussion, and thus to give that discussion some guarantee of productivity. We would like to hope that our modest efforts in this direction will not be without fruit.

ON FORMALISM IN SCHOOL MATHEMATICS TEACHING [1]

All comments known to us concerning the quality of the mathematics training of our secondary school graduates agree in one respect, that to the present time one of the most widespread and serious weaknesses of this training is *formalism* in the pupils' mathematical knowledge and techniques. This shortcoming hinders almost equally the attainment of every one of the aims that school mathematics teaching sets itself. Firstly and most acutely, it affects the immediate practical application of the knowledge and techniques acquired at school. When confronted with a real problem, a pupil who has retained from his school education only the outer, formal expressions of mathematical methods, without having mastered their essential content, will have no chance of recognizing which of these methods can be applied to the solution of the problem. He will not be able, as we say, to *formulate the problem mathematically*. To a large extent, he will also be helpless in finding its solution, since he has never developed the habit of thinking out the real meaning of the operations he performs, and consequently neither the practical demands of the problem facing him nor even its mathematical content can guide him in choosing these operations.

Formalism in mathematical knowledge hinders to no less an extent the work of secondary school graduates in the higher educational institutes. By its very nature, higher mathematics, which they meet here for the first time, does not admit of a superficial, purely formal approach. Someone who, in all his previous mathematical training, has been used to mastering only the outer expressions, to reaching only a formal understanding of mathematical concepts and truths, will be helpless when dealing with the world of variables, where nothing can be understood without the ability to link the external, formal apparatus directly with the mathematical reality standing behind it.

We must finally concede that formalism in mathematical knowledge has just as serious a consequence in the almost complete inertness and uselessness of such knowledge in forming the pupils' scientific world-view, a task which should be one of the main concerns of our general educational schools. Surely, it is hardly necessary to demonstrate that

[1]First published in the Izvestiya Akademii Pedagogicheskikh Nauk RSFSR, No. 4, 1946, under the title 'O formalizme v shkol'nom prepodavanii matematiki'.

knowledge and techniques associated only with the outward form of the studied subject, and divorced from its content, are quite incapable of influencing the pupil's moral education or of developing his outlook on the world.

In this way, a formalistic character in the pupil's mathematical knowledge and techniques does indeed represent a real obstacle in the path of achieving every one of the aims set themselves by our general educational schools. There are not and cannot be, therefore, any two opinions as to the necessity and urgency of taking arms against this phenomenon. However, if this campaign is to have some chance of success, it must not be carried out superficially, but placed on a solid, scientific basis. It would hardly be appropriate to limit oneself here to rallying the teaching profession or putting together a few hasty methodological remarks whose content would necessarily fall within the bounds of long-familiar banalities. First of all we need a thorough scientific analysis of the phenomenon against which we propose to take arms; we must reveal its essence, and identify all its characteristic features; by intensive investigations we must seek out its deep roots as well as its immediate causes; and only after all this can we pass on to the problem of setting up on a scientific basis the most effective approaches to deal with it.

In all these investigations, theoretical ideas must work hand in hand with observation and experiment. The considerable labour involved in such an approach to the problem should not deter us if we really desire to carry the fight to the finish and not to remain content with a series of amateurishly got-up patches which carry no real guarantee of holding. I think, in particular, that the mathematics section of the Institute of Educational Methods of the R.S.F.S.R. Academy of Pedagogical Sciences has every reason to make this one of its central problems for the next few years, and to bring together for its solution a number of departments from our foremost pedagogical institutes.

It must be admitted that up to the present time this problem has not even been formulated in scientific terms. In this present article I have no intention of giving any sort of final, definitive solution to even one of the problems that arise. I see my task as being something quite different: I should like my remarks to provoke as lively a discussion as possible. If in the course of this discussion it should be possible to feel out, to catch hold of the main contours of the problems we have posed, and at the same time to attract the attention of a large circle of the teaching world to these problems, then that is all I could hope to achieve.

I shall turn now to the basic problem—to the question of what constitutes formalism in mathematical knowledge. In order to reveal the essence of some complex phenomenon, it is often useful to analyse it carefully for a small number of particularly striking examples which are typical of its occurrence in practice. We shall therefore begin by listing a few such examples.

1. A pupil who is able to answer quickly and accurately the question 'what is a logarithm?' is at the same time unable, even after considerable thought, to cope with the problem 'calculate without the aid of tables $10^{\lg 7}$'.

2. A pupil who can draw correctly the graph of the logarithmic function, and has it in front of his eyes, is unable to say what happens to the logarithm of a number as that number decreases to zero.

3. A pupil who can readily solve a system of equations with unknowns x and y, is left in bewilderment if faced with the same system of equations with unknowns k and l.

4. A pupil who can prove correctly a geometrical theorem with the diagram set out in its customary form, is unable to repeat the proof for a different but equivalent setting out of the diagram.

After looking carefully at these and similar examples, we are readily convinced that in all cases of this type a characteristic feature is *a breakdown in the pupil's understanding of the correct mutual relationships between the inner content of the mathematical fact and its outward form* (its verbal, symbolic or visual and diagrammatical expression). This correct mutual relation must, of course, amount to the fact itself, i.e. its inner content, serving as the main object of attention, while the outer representation (verbal formula, symbolical notation, diagram) is only a means, a tool for remembering and conveying the factual content. In the examples we have quoted (and all similar ones) this correct mutual relationship has suffered a radical distortion. The outer representation of the mathematical fact does not hold the subordinate position that it should have by nature, but becomes an independent entity often dominating the inner content. In the first two examples, the contents of the corresponding mathematical facts were quite absent from the pupil's understanding. A pupil who is unable to find $10^{\lg 7}$ in fact *does not know* what a logarithm is, no matter how confidently he has learnt off the appropriate definition. The definition remains for him an empty phrase, unconnected with the real meaning of the concept of a logarithm (for in order to solve the required problem, it is only necessary to know what is meant by a logarithm). It is exactly the same in the second example: the pupil remembers the graph representing the behaviour of the logarithmic function, but at the same time he in fact *does not know* what this behaviour is.

We see a rather different picture in the last two examples. Here the content of the mathematical fact, the method of solving this or that problem, although it is present in the pupil's mind, appears welded to a completely fixed, congealed, unalterable outer expression; any attempt to change this outer expression for some other, equivalent, or perhaps even better expression leads to the content of the mathematical fact being lost along with its customary outer form; an arbitrary, perhaps even unsuccessfully chosen outward expression becomes the indispensible link connecting the mathematical fact with the pupil's understanding; the link is destroyed if this arbitrarily chosen outward expression is replaced by some other.

We see, therefore, that characteristic of all appearances of formalism is *a disproportionate domination in the pupil's mind of the external form* (either verbal, symbolical or diagrammatical) *of the mathematical fact over its content.* Such domination is unbalanced not only because the content of what is being studied should normally be the main object of attention, but also because the outer expression—to which in a formal approach his attention is bound—is arbitrary, one of a great number of possible equivalent outer expressions. Subordinating the real, substantial mathematical fact to one or other form of this expression amounts to taking away any firm, permanent basis from his knowledge of this fact.

We have seen that giving such disproportionate weight to the external form may have different consequences in different cases. Sometimes the external expression replaces the meaning-content, which completely drops out of the pupil's understanding; sometimes it acquires an unjustified domination over the meaning-content. But underlying all these occurrences lies one and the same cause, which we formulated precisely above, and in which, therefore, we must recognize the essence of the general phenomenon of formalism in mathematical knowledge.

In order to wage a successful battle against formalism we must take every care to avoid confusing this defect with other widespread defects in the pupils' mathematical training. In particular, formalism in mathematical knowledge is often confused with the divorce of mathematical theory from practice. This last phenomenon, which is also widespread in our school education, is, just as formalism itself, a very serious fault. However, by confusing these two defects, by blurring their essential differences, we shall only endanger our chances of successfully defeating either. Therefore it is essential to undertake a thorough analysis of the mutual relationship between formalism and the divorce of theory from practice in the pupils' mathematical training.

If we allow what is, in the circumstances, a quite permissible simplification, the matter stands as follows. In mathematics, as in any science, the original source of knowledge, its *first stage,* is the external world of objective practical experience. Relations and forms abstracted from it, i.e. the basic mathematical concepts and laws, make up the *second stage* in building the edifice of mathematics. Finally, the outer expressions of the concepts and laws, as used by the mathematician in scientific analysis—the whole arsenal of formal, symbolical notations, precise, definitive verbal formulations, and visual images—forms the *third*, exterior and formal *stage* of this building. For the mathematician, the first stage is the *source* of his researches; the second stage is the real *object* of these researches; and the third serves as their *tool*. The divorce of theory from practice represents a break-down of the link between the first and second stages, a hiatus between the mathematical researches and their living source—practical experience. On the other hand, the phenomenon of formalism is a break-down in the proper connection between the second and third stages. The tool of the research here, as it were, ceases to be a tool and becomes an end in itself, while the true object of research is to a greater or lesser extent emasculated. It is the outer, formal, symbolical expression of the basic mathematical fact that is learnt off and remembered, while the fact itself is either wholly absent from the pupils' understanding, or if it is present, is outside all links with its formal expression and quite dissociated from the formal expression in his mind.

In this way both phenomena—formalism and the divorce of theory from practice—represent a break-down of the proper links between different parts of the chain forming the stages of mathematical knowledge indicated earlier. However, the break in the chain occurs at different places in the two cases. Whereas the divorce of theory from practice represents a breakdown between the first and second stages, formalism in mathematical knowledge consists of a distortion of the proper inter-relation between the two higher stages, a disproportionate domination of the third, outer, formal stage over the second, the stage of real mathematical facts. It is clear, of course, that by fixing the pupil's attention on the outward form of mathematical facts and thereby distracting him from the content of these facts, formalism renders the pupil's whole mathematical training ineffectual: the third stage, cut off from the second, can have no contact with the first—the material world. *Directly*, however, formalism is still a loss of contact between the outer expression and the *mathematical* content of the corresponding fact, not its *material* interpretation or embodiment. Hence, in order to organize a successful attack on formalism, it is necessary scrupulously to avoid any confusion between it and the phenomenon of an immediate divorce of mathematical theory from living practice.

Sometimes one encounters even greater misunderstandings of the nature of formalism. Thus, formalism of mathematical knowledge is at times confused with the demand, necessary at all stages of mathematical science, for formal, logical rigour in making deductions. The fight against formalism is understood as an attempt to drive out from school mathematics teaching the demand for formal, logical rigour in setting up mathematical truths. It is so clear that this is just a crude vulgarization of the problem, an elementary confusion arising from a similarity in the sound of the two terms, that it is hardly worthwhile spending time on these tendencies. It is as if, by way of an attack on *idealism*, we demanded the expulsion from the school course of all *ideas*.

Still cruder vulgarizations take the form of certain statements in which, under the flag of the fight against formalism, the teaching of mathematics itself is attacked; it is put to blame on account of the abstract nature of its concepts and laws. To avoid stupid methodological and pedagogical errors, such attempts should be quashed once and for all.

In accordance with Engels' classical definition, to which modern science has nothing to add, the objects of mathematical study are the quantitative relations and spatial forms of the material world. These relations and forms make up the content of mathematical concepts— such concepts as number, equation, function, limit, point, line, angle, triangle, circle and so on. To the laws of the material world correspond connections of an abstract character between mathematical concepts— mathematical truths called axioms and theorems. Thus the fundamental concepts of mathematics, and the fundamental relations between them, are born by way of abstraction from the quantitative relations and spatial forms which are present in the material world. Conversely, the conclusions of mathematics find interpretation in the properties of objects of the external world and are used in studying these objects and putting them to practical use. All of this is an expression of the unity of theory and practice in mathematics. On the other hand, the internal development of mathematics itself, the logical growth of its concepts and the deduction of its laws, can proceed and in fact does proceed on a purely abstract plane, independently of the original material basis of these concepts and laws. The demand that is sometimes heard for preserving the connections with the material interpretation at all stages in a mathematical discussion, and the corresponding accusation against mathematical science of representing a 'divorce of theory from practice', must be considered a crude vulgarization of the Marxist point of view. Engels points this out quite clearly: 'To be in a position to study these forms and relations in their pure form, it is necessary to separate them completely from their content, leaving this to one side as something irrelevant'[1].

After such considerations concerning the nature of formalism, we must turn to the question of locating the causes of this phenomenon. Clearly, these causes may find their roots either in the character of the

[1] "F. Engels", M. Anti-Dyuring, Gospolitizdat, 1948, p. 37.

material that is taught (i.e. in *what* we teach the schoolchildren) or in
the teaching methods (i.e. in *how* we teach the schoolchildren). I think
that we would all agree that in actual fact there exist causes of both
types, and differences in opinion can only arise over the question of
the relative importance of these two groups of causes. In my opinion
the basic, determining causes are already present in the character of
the course material, the choice of which has a tendency to cultivate
the formal type of knowledge irrespective of the teaching methods.
It may be that it is not so much the actual text of our syllabuses that is
at fault as the traditional interpretation of this text, the tradition of
emphasizing certain (formal) aspects at the cost of ignoring others
(of more basic importance); however, even the unambiguous textual
content of our syllabuses plays an important role. As far as methods
of teaching are concerned, here too there are many features which are
capable of encouraging formalistic tendencies, although their role in
this process is surely less important than that of the syllabus material.
To develop some arguments in support of my opinion, I shall now note
down a number of points, both in the syllabus material and in the
traditional methodological approaches, which in my view are capable
of giving rise to or accentuating a formal character in the pupils'
knowledge and habits. The points I shall note down must be taken
merely as examples; they have no pretension to exhaustiveness.

1. Even in a brief glance through our syllabuses one is struck by
the fact that a number of sections are devoid of clear motivation. This
defect is so much a part of the syllabus material itself that not even the
most able methodologist would have the power to correct it. This
applies in particular to the algebra course and certain parts of the
trigonometry course. It is well known how important a place is given
to so-called 'algebraic transformations' in the algebra course. There
can be no doubt that an easy mastery of algebraic transformations enters
into the number of those elementary techniques which are essential for
every schoolchild to know; but is it really possible to believe that the
best way of imparting these techniques is that represented by our
present practice—of day by day repetition for months on end of
algebraic transformations for the sake of algebraic transformations,
with never a mention of why this should be necessary? The pupils are
set to factorize an endless string of polynomials, making use of the most
ingenious methods, but with never an indication of what all this is for.
More than this, in the whole section on algebraic transformations there
is not a single mention or even a hint as to the motivation. It is clear
that any one expression can be transformed in a great number of
different ways; it is quite unclear just which of these ways is in view
when the pupil is asked to 'transform' this expression; it is equally
unclear why he should have to choose this particular transformation

and not some other; and we have still said nothing of the fact that the pupil is never told why in general it is necessary to transform the given expression. We meet exactly the same absence of any general directive in problems on proving trigonometrical identities.

Further, the introduction of complex numbers into the school course remains almost completely without motivation. Historically speaking, it is well known that these bizarre and paradoxical numbers (as they seem to the schoolchild), won their path into the light with great difficulty, after a long struggle which ended only when it became clear that it was natural and indeed essential to include these numbers among the objects of mathematical research. But within the bounds of the school course, this realization cannot be brought home to the pupils, and no matter how we organize the teaching, complex numbers will remain a fanciful section of the course, devoid of any natural motivation.

And how do matters stand as regards the binomial theorem? The short, simple expression $(a + b)^n$ is for some reason transformed, with the aid of very intricate discussions, into another, long, cumbersome, and hard to memorize formula, which, however, the pupil is obliged to memorize in every detail. Moreover, for the sake of this transformation he has to make a preliminary study of a whole abstract and difficult section—combinatorics (which have no other applications or connections in the school course). The binomial formula itself does not have a single application within the limits of the school course, and for those pupils who will not go on to study higher mathematics, it will remain a clear example of great efforts expended to no purpose.[1]

Have we any reason to be surprised if in such circumstances school mathematics teaching becomes a hot-bed of formalism? Can we expect that even the best teaching will implant into the pupils' minds firmly and in their true essence mathematical concepts, laws and approaches, the aims of which remain incomprehensible, which do not arouse any independent interest, and which within the bounds of the school course have not a single significant application? To argue thus would be to ignore the most rudimentary laws in the psychology of learning. Even we working mathematicians know from personal experience that of facts learnt this way in the past, at best the outer, formal expressions remain in our memory. There are far less grounds to suppose that we could fix in the still undisciplined mind of a schoolchild a mathematical

---

[1] It would be a good thing in our opinion if instead of this formula (or at least alongside it) the syllabus contained the elements of probability theory—lively and from the formal point of view quite simple material which provides a far more convincing application of combinatorial formulae and at the same time admits of many immediate practical applications.

fact which, by its position in the syllabus, can never arouse his interest and with which he can never work actively or with a clear motivation. In such cases, it is psychologically inevitable that the pupil's mind will move along the line of least resistance—at best, he will try to retain in his memory the external formal expressions of mathematical laws the real contents of which escape him on account of their unreality.

2. In the last few years certain of the most important questions of the algebra course, previously dispersed among various sections of the syllabus, have been singled out as independent topics. Among these are the study of functional dependence, the theory of inequalities, and the study of equations. This separation followed the recognition that these topics were of particular importance, and had the aim of making their study more systematic and the pupils' knowledge of them firmer and deeper. However, the effect of these reforms was exactly the opposite of what had been hoped for. The reasons for this have been very convincingly laid bare in a paper by one of our best methodologists —I. F. Sludskii. It appears that our teachers as a whole understood this separation as a prohibition to discuss these topics in other parts of the course. And with what result? We all know to how large an extent almost all sections of elementary mathematics gain in clarity, transparency, concreteness, usefulness and attractiveness when they are illuminated and penetrated by the idea of functional dependence. But now: equations of the first degree without the linear function, equations of the second degree without the quadratic function, logarithms without the logarithmic function, general indices without the exponential function; even in trigonometry, the functional point of view has largely been emasculated. This short-sighted manoeuvre— the removal from such varied material of just that element that warmed them with the breath of life, with a living and real mobility, with a rhythm that cannot be packed into any lifeless, stagnant scheme—this short-sighted manoeuvre brought with it (and to this time maintains) a considerable formalization in the approach to the main themes of the algebra and trigonometry courses, and by the same token helped to develop formalism in the pupils' knowledge.

It is the same story, though to a somewhat lesser extent, with the theory of inequalities and the study of equations. Here again we have two circles of ideas which would be capable of imparting significant actuality and weight to any part of the course. And yet we know cases where our teachers thought that they did not have the right to make use of the signs $<$ and $>$ (which could usefully be introduced even in classes I and II) since 'inequalities will be covered later'. Equations themselves should be studied with the solution of those equations at all stages of the course. Just how much such an approach can do to increase the actuality and interest of the course is shown convincingly by the question-book of Ober and Papalieu[1], where this approach is adopted consistently.

3. Turning now to the geometry course, I believe, in agreement with many other opinions on this subject, that the system we have adopted whereby a 'systematic' study (i.e. a study pretending to formal logical rigour) of geometry is started in the sixth year, is at bottom unsatisfactory, and in particular paves the way for the growth of formalism in the pupils' knowledge. In the first place, formal logical proofs are given to the children at an age when their thinking habits have not yet matured, when a visual inspection still carries complete conviction. This effort to force the pupils beyond the natural limitations of their age leads only to the result that they feel the formal, logical basis of obvious truths to be something essentially unnecessary, a form of tortuous wizardry that has to be followed only because it is part of the school programme and in order to avoid bad marks. First of all, such a situation inevitably disturbs the authority of the teaching, and then, just as inevitably, leads to the schoolchild tackling these unnecessary (as he sees them) discussions along the line of least resistance, preserving in his memory only their outer, formal structure. Even we professional mathematicians know how hard it is to remember the proofs of precisely those propositions that are most obvious, and just how much mathematical culture is needed before such proofs can be mastered at the appropriate level. In the second place, the system of teaching geometry customary here causes the pupils to spend whole years grinding through dull material which provides but meagre food for the geometrical imagination—parallel and perpendicular lines in the plane, mutual configurations of lines and planes in space, etc. It is only in their final years that they have the chance to meet any geometrical images capable of producing an immediate, clear-cut impression—circles, ellipses, cylinders, cones, pyramids, polyhedra, etc. Again and again we come up against the situation where everything that could help to create a lively, active interest in the subject has, as if deliberately, been left out of the material appropriate to any given age; with it goes all that makes for a real and not a formal understanding of the subject. Conversely what is retained and cultivated is just that which at the given age produces a quite natural revulsion.

Such, in my opinion, are the main defects of the syllabus material which lead to formalism in the pupils' mathematical knowledge. What should and can be done to correct them? The answer to this question ought to be quite clear from what has preceded. It is essential first to give a clear motivation for those parts of the course where this can be done easily, and has not been done up to the present time. An excellent

[1]P. Ober and G. Papalieu, 'Exercises in Elementary Algebra', Russian edition (1940).

example of how this can be achieved is the setting out of the section on transformations of rational functions in the recent algebra course of Alexandrov and Kolmogorov. Here, from the very beginning, the general aims of all such transformations are clearly stated—the reduction of any rational expression to the ratio of two polynomials. The relative simplicity of this last form provides in the schoolchild's eyes an adequate motive for the transformations, and in each separate example shows him what he should aim for and why.

Sections of the syllabus that find no adequate applications within the bounds of the school programme, and consequently cannot be mastered with the necessary effectiveness, conviction or activeness, no matter how much methodological pressure is applied, should be reconsidered with a view to removing them completely from the current syllabuses. I shall allow myself the temerity to recommend not having too many scruples in this matter; those pupils who will be studying mathematics in the higher schools will master the rejected sections to much greater effect there, where these sections will receive a large number of concrete and convincing applications, come alive in the pupils' minds, and turn into useful tools for their scientific work.

Secondly, it is necessary that the idea of functional dependence should penetrate almost all the algebra course, the final part of the arithmetic course, and a considerable part of the trigonometry course. We all know very well that even in the higher schools (in the mathematics faculties of the universities and pedagogical institutes) a course in the study of functions helps, more than any other, to outgrow the habit of adopting a formal attitude to mathematical concepts, and to create a lively interest in and an active, creative attitude towards them. The reason for this is clear: in the theory of functions, the formal apparatus plays a minimal role, and a person who could only take in the outer form of mathematical facts would here be unable to move a single step forward; on the other hand, the dynamic idea of a variable is in essence ideally suited to the breaking up of any petrified forms. As the founders of Marxism have several times explained, it is indeed with this very idea that dialectics enters mathematics—it is the best instrument for the fight against all sorts of formalistic deviations.

Similarly, operations on inequalities should be incorporated into all parts of the mathematics course, since the concepts 'greater than' and 'less than' themselves will necessarily be associated in the schoolchildrens' minds with concrete, living, full-blooded ideas. The inequality signs and the simplest properties of inequalities can be learnt even at the earliest stages, and such a mastery, given the proper methodological approach, should undoubtedly have considerable effect. However, the solution of inequalities containing unknowns must be taken together with the solution of equations of the corresponding degree. In exactly the same way, at all stages of the course, the general study of an equation should be undertaken together with its solution. In particular, the solution of any literal equation, if accompanied by a detailed study of the equation, would take on a much more real and solid image in the pupils' minds, and would necessarily be torn out of the formal setting where it might otherwise stagnate. It is also relevant to note that dividing off the study of equations into a separate topic is unsatisfactory if only because no text-book gives—or could give—a sensible answer to the question of what is the study of equations; in practice, this term is understood in completely different ways, in different cases, and these could never be put together into a unified general scheme.

Finally, I would consider it necessary to introduce quite radical changes into the arrangement of the geometry course. In the seven-year schools the geometry course should be begun as early as possible, at least within the first few classes, and continued to the end of the seven-year training.[1] The structure of this course should be determined by contextual and teaching considerations, and not by formal or logical considerations. There are no obstacles to prevent the children becoming acquainted with the simplest properties of polyhedra, circular bodies, etc., even at the earliest stages of the course.[2] Naturally, this course must be based on an open and explicit refusal in principle to demand formal, logical proofs. This does not mean that proofs should be avoided everywhere; but they should be introduced with extreme caution and very gradually, and only at those points where the pupils themselves can appreciate the need for such a proof; it is clear that this would demand special preparation and great pedagogical tact. At the beginning logical proofs should be completely absent; then, later on, they should start to make their appearance, rarely at first, but with increasing frequency. And not before the seventh class would I consider it possible to begin the so-called 'systematic' geometry course, where all conclusions are logically grounded. I have no doubt that, if the geometry course were to be set out in this way (which, incidentally, is no methodological innovation but is frequently met with in other countries), the unhappy phenomenon of formalism in geometrical knowledge would be encountered considerably less often than it is at present.

Let us pass on now to the questions of locating those prevailing teaching traditions which may be helping to foster the growth of forma-listic tendencies, and of describing how they should be changed in order

[1]At the time when this article was written, only the seven-year course was compulsory (B.G.).
[2]These sections are included in the syllabus for the eight-year schools (B.G.).

that the pupils' knowledge should have maximum real content and effectiveness. Something in this direction follows from what we have said already. We do not take enough care to set before the pupils the aim of the mathematical operations they perform or of the concepts and laws they have to master. And even in those cases where we feel that the motivation and essential content of the section of the course under study have been adequately explained, we are too ready to leave it at that, without seeing the necessity, when solving particular problems or proofs, of emphasizing again and again the underlying motivation, of indicating the role and significance of the theorem being proved in the general plan of the section, of elucidating its connections and mutual relations with concepts, assertions and problems taken earlier. No time or effort should be spared in all this, for a clear picture in the pupils' minds, of the links between different parts of the general theory helps greatly in mastering the real, essential content of these separate parts. To understand 'which is for what' is always a dependable vaccination against formalism.

However, this is not the most important thing. If we carefully analyse our own experience, we would all unanimously agree that only those scientific facts regularly remain firmly and actively rooted in our memories which at some time were the object or the tool of our own work, our own creative activity. A book or article, even if it has been read three times through, will inevitably be forgotten if its material has only been absorbed passively, if its contents have never been the raw material or the tool of our own active, creative work.

As for myself, many years' experience long ago induced me to develop the habit of working in the following manner. If I am interested in mastering and preserving in my memory the contents of some scientific article—its real essence and not only its formal contents—I put it aside after I have read it, and with pencil and paper attempt to reproduce its contents, changing where possible the steps of the author's argument into others which are more peculiar or customary to me, always introducing new notation that seems to me more natural or convenient, and paraphrasing or even reformulating particular propositions; sometimes in this process I rewrite distinct links in the argument in the form of special lemmas. After all this has been more or less satisfactorily accomplished, I start to think over what new questions arise in connection with the results of the article I have been working on. All the problems that come into my mind I write down carefully as questions, and try to solve them, continuing these attempts until I have been able to get a feel of the particular difficulty in each of the listed questions. It is only after all this work has been carried out that I can be sure of some guarantee that in the moment of need the content of the article I have worked over will come into my memory as a working tool ready for use, and will not remain a dead weight mastered only in a formal manner and not capable of any useful application.

I do not, of course, wish to suggest that this path should be followed by the schoolchild in studying the syllabus material. I have given such a detailed description only in order to show that even a mathematical scholar finds that his mind will take in firmly and genuinely only those things on which he has actively worked. It is absolutely clear that there are much greater grounds for supposing that this rule holds in relation to the schoolchild's still unformed and undisciplined apparatus for absorbing new results. The pupil himself does not know it, as yet he has no experience, and it is not he who should be blamed for learning jumbles off by heart, but his teacher. The hard-working schoolchild may read one and the same piece many times on end, making a tremendous effort to memorize it as best as he can, so that he ends up by willy-nilly learning whole paragraphs off by heart; yet in a week's time it appears that the content of the memorized material has completely blown out of his mind, and there remain only the dead phrases and formulae that he has learnt off by heart. We commit a methodological crime if we do not supervise his work on the studied material with appropriate pedagogical tact and skill. To the maximum possible extent, all our pedagogical efforts must be directed towards making the schoolchild take in the material while he is actively at work on it, and we must use all possible means to imbue this work with the elements of self-reliance and even the smallest germ of creative activity, constantly calling to mind that the most enthusiastic, determined, and concentrated efforts on the pupil's part will give him nothing save lifeless formal knowledge if it consists only of passive assimilation. The pupil must learn only during the process of seeking, of intellectually active work, of independently overcoming difficulties—in this lies the only, but at the same time an absolutely reliable, guarantee that his knowledge will not be purely formal.

The question of how to achieve all this in respect of the given syllabus material is, in my opinion, the central methodological problem of every school discipline. Of course I have no intention of trying to study the solution of this problem here; such a solution can be achieved only after many years' work and thought by a large group of methodologists. There are, however, some particular methodological approaches which we almost always ignore, and which nonetheless, as it seems to me, could contribute significantly towards a successful solution of the stated problem if they were taken up on a sufficiently wide scale. I should like to say a little about these approaches.

We must use all means, even those which might appear to be the most insignificant details, in order to try and stimulate, encourage, and when possible even provocate any appearance of independence in the pupil's approach to the studied material. It must become a habit for the schoolchild to choose notation different to that used in the text-book or by the teacher, to draw up a diagram differently than in the text-book; all this could be requested directly, and certain of our best teachers do so already. Independent rephrasings of definitions and formulations of theorems (on condition, of course, that these re-phrasings are completely equivalent), the inclusion of an independent element in some discussion, or the working out of an original method of solving a problem, should be held up in front of the whole class as real achievements. This would seem to be all too obvious, and yet in fact how far are we from achieving it! For it is no rarity in our schools for not only the pupil, but even the teacher, to be forbidden to prove a theorem otherwise than it is proved in the text-book. With us, as a rule, the teacher demands from the pupil that all problems of a given section should be solved by the same rubric, and any sign of independence is stifled.

There is no doubt about the harmfulness of the tradition that has taken root here of standardizing notation. One has only to think for a little to realise how far we would have moved along the path of fighting formalism in the solution of equations if our pupils tackled the solution of systems of equations with unknowns a and b, or k and 1, with the same ease that they tackle them when the unknowns are denoted by x and y; if I were to compile a problem book in algebra, in each new equation I would label the unknowns differently. And yet in arithmetic here we even use the phrase 'problems with x's', which to any mathe-matically cultured ear produces an impression close to a scandal of vulgarity. Nor is it in any way necessary always to denote the general term in a progression by a_n; in the next case let it be t_r or u_k.

The pupils should be required to learn as little as possible by heart. It is useful to learn verses by heart. But in mathematics to learn definitions and theorems off by heart is only necessary at the early stages of education; as soon as the pupils have grown up to the extent that they can express something 'in their own words', not only should they be given the right to do so, but this right should be made into an obligation. In one and the same class, let the pupils who can do so formulate a proposition themselves, and those who cannot, learn it off by heart; at the same time let the teacher make it clear that the achieve-ments of the first group are more valuable and of a higher order than those of the second—this would lead to healthy and useful com-petition. A particularly dismal impression is produced by mass learning by heart of 'definitions' which are not definitions at all, but quite unassuming descriptions (the 'definition' of a number, a point, a line, an angle, etc.).

The reader may express some doubt as to the effectiveness of steps which concern such relatively insignificant matters as notations, formulations, etc. I think that any stimulus to independence in such 'details', representing, of course, only the first stage of the teacher's care to foster in the schoolchildren an active approach towards their subject, has even in itself quite considerable significance. In such 'details' the character of the pupil is formed, and the habit is cultivated of responding to every question with albeit uncomplicated but nevertheless active working of his own mind. One can give an answer in terms of a learnt-off definition while understanding nothing of its meaning; but one cannot define in one's own words or even describe a concept whose essential meaning is missing from one's comprehension. The pupil who knows how to prove a theorem for any disposition of the diagram, thereby discovers that he has learnt its real geometrical content. In all these cases we have made no small progress along the road in the fight against formalism.

Another important weapon in the battle for genuine knowledge could be certain changes in the character of the examination requirements. The questions must be set in such a way that a satisfactory answer to them can only be given if the subject has been understood properly and not merely in a formal manner. The sense of this requirement is very obvious and it would not be difficult to carry out; I shall illustrate by an example. Some years ago I happened to be present at the graduation examinations of one of the Moscow schools. The girl, whose ticket contained the Binomial Theorem, wrote out a long series of equations on the blackboard. The teacher, glancing quickly at the equations, said 'What you have written is correct. You may go.' I interrupted, and requested her to explain how the second equation followed from the first, the third from the second, and so on. I obtained no answer to any of these questions, although I waited for them for some considerable time. I have some grounds for considering that such formalism in the examination requirements has become quite typical with us, and in fact not only in examinations, but also in the lessons. Is it really necessary to say that this must inevitably bring in its wake a formal character in the pupil's knowledge? Is it not clear that if the pupil is made to understand that, both in the lessons and in the examinations, he will be required to show a true and not merely a formal understanding of the subject, then in his own work also he will receive a significant stimulus towards understanding its real content? At all places and at all times questions must be asked in such a way that the answer should show absolutely clearly whether the pupil really knows what he is being asked about, or whether he has merely learnt by heart a series of symbols or verbal expressions; and it is very important that the pupils should know beforehand that the questions will be set in just this manner.

It remains for me to remind the reader of the request I made in the introduction to this article: to look on this modest work of mine as only a first contribution towards the important and difficult problems of studying the nature and sources of formalism in the pupils' mathematical knowledge, and of seeking out the most effective lines of attack on this basic defect in the mathematical training given by our secondary schools. I could not and did not wish to give any final answers. I should like my remarks to raise as many critical comments as possible, with the hope that the ensuing discussion will generate a solution of these problems and allow the grave defect of formalism in our schools to be overcome, thereby raising significantly the standard of the pupils' mathematical training.

ON THE EDUCATIVE EFFECT OF MATHEMATICS LESSONS [1]

The aim of mathematics, in contrast to most other subjects, is not the direct examination of the objects which make up the external world around us, but the study of their quantitative relations and spatial forms. This peculiarity of mathematics explains the greater part of those well-known difficulties in teaching mathematics which inevitably confront the mathematics teacher and are almost unknown to teachers of other sciences. A formidable problem which faces the mathematics teacher is to overcome, in the pupils' minds, the instinctively arising sense of the 'dryness', the formal character, and the remoteness from everyday life of his science. Much that is valuable and useful has been written about this, and we are fully aware of how the better masters of our schools handle this problem.

At the same time, this same feature of mathematics largely explains the particular difficulties faced by the mathematics teacher who wishes to use his lessons for purposes of a general educative nature. It is clear that here also his problem is more difficult than is the case with most other subjects. A science which is concerned not with the study of things themselves but only the relationships between them, thereby making necessary a certain degree of abstraction, obviously gives fewer opportunities for the teacher to exercise an effective influence on the formation of the character and outlook of his pupils, or on their behaviour. Without a doubt, this explains why very little, if anything, has been said about mathematics lessons in investigations concerned with the general educative function of school studies.

The little which has been written on this subject does not give rise to any basic objections. The matter is usually reduced to two key factors of educational influence; on the one hand, it is said that the logical rigour and elegant deductive reasoning characteristic of mathematics are bound to teach the children a general logical culture in their habits of thinking; on the other hand, it is pointed out that a proper choice of the subject-matter of mathematical problems offers wide opportunities for the communication of facts and figures capable of broadening the pupils' outlook, raising their general cultural level, and influencing the patriotic aspects of their political and ideological education.

[1]First published in Matematicheskoe Prosveshchenie Vol. 6 (1961) under the title "O vospitatel'nom effekte urokov matematiki".

77

D

This is undeniably true, but I think that it is far from being the whole story.

First of all, no mention at all is made here of some most important aspects of moral education for which, it seems to me, mathematics lessons offer the most tangible means. Further, the important problem of teaching a logical habit of thought, to which much attention is usually given, is nevertheless treated in most cases tritely, superficially, and inadequately. The examples given often do not rise above the level of common cliche and are, therefore, very ineffective.

Finally, although it must be used wherever possible, the educative influence of facts presented in text-book problems is linked with the mathematical content of the lessons only in the most superficial manner. It is clear that in this case it is not mathematics itself, nor its laws and style, which provides the educative influence, but certain facts which are associated with it in a purely external way, which serve only as a frame for the text-book problems, and which, without any alterations to the mathematical content of the problem, could be replaced by any other analogous facts. It will be understood therefore, that strictly speaking, this key feature of educational influence, important and efficacious as it is, cannot be considered as part of the school programme in mathematics as such.

All the above remarks indicate that as yet we are far from having taken a sufficiently thorough appraisal of the educational importance of mathematics lessons. The present article sets out to provide some answer to this question. For this purpose, in what follows I shall look briefly at a number of factors which, up to the present time, and as far as I can judge, have either been neglected entirely in seeking out the educative possibilities of mathematics lessons, or have been dealt with only superficially.

Culture in Thinking

Accurate Thinking

The role and importance of mathematics in teaching the habit of disciplined and accurate thinking is so widely acknowledged that it is frequently stated that the teaching of a rigorous and logical sequence of thought is the primary and basic problem of a mathematics teacher; in comparison, even the pupils' knowledge of the contents of mathematics is sometimes relegated to a secondary position (without a doubt, this must be recognized as a harmful extreme). Nevertheless, just because this educative function of mathematics has come to acquire a banal character, we hear many stereotyped statements made without giving sufficient thought to the subject. As a rule (and it sometimes sets one's teeth on edge) attention is concentrated on a few customary points which, although important, are nevertheless both particular and limited in their significance—such as, for example, the already notorious distinction between direct and inverse theorems. In the meantime, questions of greater importance are overshadowed.

I think that the main aspect of the educative function of mathematics lessons is to train the pupils to realize the full value of argumentation; and on this aspect most of the rest depends.

In everyday life, even in 'amateur' (not strictly scientific) discussions we are usually content with only one or two arguments to defend some assertion we have made. The opponent may draw upon several arguments to oppose our statement. But in general, neither his argument nor ours is fully conclusive; both sides continue to look for new arguments in support of their view, and so the discussion continues.

This is roughly the way in which even scientific discussions are carried on in those fields of knowledge which are not counted among the so-called 'exact' sciences; of course the arguments here are, as a rule, fuller than in everyday discussions; but almost never is it possible to make them exhaustive, open to no objection, and thereby put an end to the discussion.

Matters are somewhat different in mathematics. Here, if an argument permits even the slightest possibility of well-founded criticism, if it is not completely and absolutely conclusive, it is mercilessly condemned, and discarded as lacking even the slightest force. In mathematics, there are no, and cannot be, 'half-proven' or 'almost-proven' statements. Either the argument is so perfect that further discussion on the question is no longer possible, or there is no such argument.

When studying mathematics, the pupil for the first time in his life comes across a very important requirement—to make his argumentation perfect. In the beginning, this requirement surprises, repels and frightens him. But gradually, day by day, he becomes accustomed to it. The good teacher can do much to quicken this process and make it more productive. He should teach his pupils to practise mutual criticism; when one of them presents or works out some problem in front of the class, all the others must try strenuously to find possible objections and state them quickly. If the pupil who is 'defending' himself against all such objections can force his critics to be silent, he will certainly feel, and deserve, the joy of victory. Once he has experienced this, he will quickly realize that it was the logical perfection of his argument that gave him the means to achieve this victory. And he will naturally strive more determinedly and persistently to achieve perfection of argumentation not only in mathematics but in all sorts of other discussions. Every time he is faced with a problem, he will try as far as possible to disarm his opponents by using, to the fullest extent, the whole stock of arguments which are applicable to the particular situation.

This educative process is of great importance in the development of logical thinking, particularly if it is realized that it becomes habitual for the pupil to seek tirelessly for perfection of argumentation not only in discussion, but also in his individual thinking. This process is taking place daily before our eyes in many thousands of pupils. It arises spontaneously and develops in its own way without our special interference. Nevertheless, we clearly do not have the right to let it drift on its own, for we have it in our power to increase the riches and durability of this process, to make it faster and more complete. Once we are able to do this, then it is obvious that we must. The question of which methods are the most effective in achieving this goal is, however, a problem of teaching which we cannot examine in detail here.

In the course of the pupil's intellectual development, the general principle of the struggle to achieve perfection of argumentation takes on many typical concrete forms, the most important of which we shall now enumerate.

(1) *The struggle to avoid false generalizations*

The naturalist, having observed the presence of some quality (mark) in a number of individuals of a given species, can with a clear scientific conscience regard this quality as being common to all members of the species he has examined. No one reproaches him for this—inductive conclusions of this type are one of the basic methods of the natural sciences. Of course, even in these sciences, co-ordinating and interpretive theoretical considerations are both permissible and necessary. Nevertheless, the starting point and the final, definitive testing of any hypothesis in these sciences will always remain observation and experiment on particular examples.

There is a basic difference in mathematics. If we verify that for tens (or even millions) of triangles, which we have chosen at random, some property always makes its appearance, we still do not have the right to attribute this property to *all* triangles. Such a conclusion would not have been tested to the end, and in mathematics, everything which is not valid in this way is considered as being incorrect. Certainty that the given feature exists as a general property of *all* triangles can only result from a conclusive, general *proof*.

What can and should the pupil learn from that stern criticism of incompletely founded generalizations which he will meet in mathematics? Naturally, he must not try to carry over such requirements to the conclusions of other sciences and, even more particularly, to the practical situations of life. The need for absolute completeness of induction is peculiar to the mathematical approach, and is completely unrealizable either in the natural sciences or in practical life. Nevertheless, the habit of verifying the truth of each generalization carefully and thoroughly, the habit of bearing in mind that what has been observed in many cases is not thereby necessarily true in all cases, and hence that regularities based upon (even very many) individual observations and experiments require ever further verification—all these most important habits of method, necessary in any scientific and practical activity, are greatly developed and strengthened as the pupil's mathematical culture increases.

It is a process we see taking place every day before our eyes.

(2) *The struggle to avoid ill-founded analogies*

Conclusions by analogy are a customary and correct means of establishing new laws, as much in the empirical sciences as in everyday life. If, say, the naturalist recalls that all the species he has seen up to now possessing the signs A and B, have also the sign C, and if he then discovers a new species showing the signs A and B, he would naturally conclude that this new species also possesses the sign C. Such a conclusion by analogy becomes still more convincing if, as often happens, to the number of empiricial facts described above are added some theoretical grounds for supposing that the joint appearance of the signs A, B and C occurs not by chance but as the realization of some important general principle. But only in mathematics is it possible— and in fact absolutely necessary—to require that these considerations of principle are developed to the stage of a comprehensive proof. Either we strictly prove that, because signs A and B are present, sign C must necessarily also be present; or, if we are unable to obtain a complete proof, we are forbidden to make any conclusion whatever about sign C because of the presence of signs A and B. But even in the first case (that is, when the theorem 'from A and B follows C' is proved) the simple application of this general theorem to a particular concrete case could hardly be called a 'conclusion by analogy'. Thus it is correct to say that, in mathematics, conclusions by analogy are categorically forbidden (which must not, of course, be taken as diminishing the immense heuristic importance of conclusions by analogy), while in the empirical sciences and practical activity, conclusions by analogy have a worthy role as one of the basic means of developing new laws. Because of this, the question again arises of what contribution mathematics can make in this direction towards the development of a general culture in thinking. And again we must reply as we did before: a mathematical training, accustoming the mind to the thought that conclusions by analogy can serve only as a heuristic method which, by itself, still does not possess the force of a proof, must teach the student to treat such conclusions with extreme caution in other fields of thought, to ever bear in mind that it is impossible without a complete examination to consider the resulting conclusion as unshakeably established. At one time or another, each of us has experienced the educational influence of this feature of mathematical thought, and each day we note how it helps to further the thought development of our pupils. A critical attitude towards conclusions by analogy is one of the most important qualities distinguishing an educatedly scientific and practical way of thinking from one which is primitive and Philistine. The study of mathematics will always serve as one of the most important means of developing this valuable quality.

(3) *The struggle for full disjunction*

When the mathematician proves some general property of all triangles, he must sometimes produce separate proofs for acute- and obtuse-angled triangles. It is well known how often beginners make mistakes in such cases, particularly when the discussion is accompanied by reference to a sketch. An acute angle is drawn, for example, and the argument relies upon supplementary considerations which are either impossible, or lose their force in the proof, if an obtuse-angled triangle is chosen. Such an argument is recognized in mathematics as being invalid, because the basic requirement of full disjunction has been broken—not all the possible variations of a given situation have been provided for, and one of them has been dropped from the field of vision

In everyday, unscientific discussions this requirement is broken at every stage. Having examined one or two very frequent or particularly obvious variations of a given situation, and having been convinced that in each of these variations we inevitably find some condition A, we conclude that this condition A is a corollary of the given situation in all cases, although in fact the situation may still have dozens of other variations besides the two or three known to us, and among the variations left out of our count there may well be some in which the presence of A is not required at all. We say, for example, that the pupil Ivanov in general cannot be disciplined because neither flattery nor threats have any effect on him. We forget by this that not all disciplinary measures have been exhausted by the failure of flattery and threats, that there still exists, for example, the method of quiet persuasion, and that perhaps our division suffers from being incomplete. We often observe a beginner who, having examined some equation for the case that a given coefficient is positive, and then for the case that this coefficient is negative, thereby considers that he has studied all cases, forgetting that the given coefficient may be zero. Here also we see an incomplete disjunction, which may lead, and often does lead, to serious errors in the conclusions.

In contrast to the two requirements that we studied earlier, the requirement of making a full disjunction, of taking into account all possible variations of a given situation, appears as a necessary property of all correct arguments, not only in mathematics. An argument in which all possibilities are not listed must always leave room for well-grounded objections and therefore cannot be accepted as fully conclusive. A military leader directing some manoeuvre must foresee in the consequences of his actions all possible counter-moves of the enemy; overlooking even one of them may mean disaster. The juridical code must in each article anticipate all reasonable variations of a given situation, or it forces the judge to make an arbitrary decision.

But nowhere does the requirement for unimpeachable accuracy of disjunction stand out so clearly and categorically as in mathematics, and no one attacks an omission in disjunction so quickly and mercilessly as a trained mathematician. That is why mathematics lessons can, and indeed do, teach the pupil this most important law of correct argumentation to an incomparably greater extent than the study of other subjects.

(4) *The struggle for complete and consistent classification*

It is not only the learned theoretician in his study who classifies; very often the practical worker also must undertake this sort of work—the engineer, the doctor, the teacher, the statistician, the agronomist. It is generally acknowledged that when classifying, the untrained mind is inclined to make many typical mistakes. The most widespread of these are the failure to make the classification *complete* and the failure to make it *consistent* (single-principled). A failure to make the classification complete occurs when some concepts remain outside the specified classes, and cannot be placed in any of them; clearly, this represents a failure to enumerate all the classes. As simple examples: to the question 'which plants do you know?', the pupil replies 'grass and trees', forgetting shrubs, lichen, and many other types; military units are divided into land, sea and air forces (leaving out the commissary, communications unit, and many others); natural numbers are divided into prime and composite numbers (leaving out the number 1); real numbers are divided into positive and negative numbers (leaving out zero).

The need to achieve complete classification is formally analogous to the need to make a full disjunction, which we examined above, but differs from it in its content. In the former case, we spoke about the need to enumerate all the different variations that may occur in some situation; here we are concerned with enumerating all the various forms of some concept. But in both cases there is a clearer and more implacable demand for completeness in mathematics than in all the other sciences, and for this reason mathematics lessons more than all others train the pupil in this essential element of accurate thinking.

A *consistent* classification means a classification carried through in terms of a single principle, a single quality. This requirement, which is strictly obligatory in all rigorous thinking, is often broken, not only in day-to-day arguments but also in serious discussions. Here are some examples of such inconsistent classifications: ships are divided into rowing boats, sailing boats, motor boats and warships. It is obvious that the classification has been based on the various means of propulsion, and the final item breaks this principle. A second example: footwear is divided into leather, canvas, rubber and fashion shoes—it is the same story here. Naturally, such a list does not always pretend to the role of a classification, and in such cases the observance of a single principle is not obligatory (for example, a declaration: the factory offers work to carpenters, plasterers, women and youths). But whenever a classifying function is attributed to such an enumeration, inconsistency of the dividing principle may well cause the whole scheme to become so vague that it will lead to theoretical confusion and a practical muddle. For this reason, the failure to achieve consistency in making a classification appears, to the logically trained mind, as an important defect in judgement. Once again, mathematics is the science most aware of this defect, and it is especially in the course of his mathematics lessons, therefore, that the pupil develops the inner duty to see that every classification is consistent and based upon a single classifying principle.

I have enumerated those aspects of the fight for accurate thinking and perfection of argumentation which seem to me most important. As I have already mentioned, I cannot in this article enter into the discussion of those teaching methods by the help of which the mathematics teacher may achieve greatest success in training his pupils in those aspects of accurate thinking I have enumerated. But I consider it necessary to make on this question one practical comment of a general nature (it will, I am sure, be completely obvious to the experienced teacher). All those requirements for accurate thinking of which I have spoken must be absorbed by the pupil gradually, from case to case, without any superfluous emphasis. Nor can there be any talk of devoting a special lesson to, say, the struggle against false analogy. Such an approach would only hopelessly destroy the desired effect. On the contrary, it is necessary to avoid general statements in every possible way, and to direct the attention of the pupils to this or that logical aspect exclusively by the use of clearly convincing, concrete mathematical material. The requirement of perfect argumentation must not be exacted through constant annoying reminders of the need for perfection, but through the illustration of concrete examples (which arise in almost every lesson) where non-observance of this requirement leads to mistakes and discrepancies. We should not preach perfection of argumentation in the abstract, but show the pupil that each gap in the argument quickly calls forth a carping question from the teacher or, what is much better, from his fellow-pupils.

I am not going to discuss here the need to use mathematics lessons for giving a correct understanding of the differences between direct and inverse statements, and many similar distinctions. On the one hand, so much has been said about this that I could hardly contribute anything new here. On the other hand, it seems to me that this sort of question, necessary as it is for logically accurate thinking, nevertheless, by its particular, specialized character, does not have such an important significance outside mathematics as those more general principles which I have listed above.

Style of Thought

Besides its specific and very strict requirements concerning the logical accuracy of deductions, mathematics is further distinguished from the other subjects taught in school by its style of thought. Although this style has undergone quite significant changes over periods of centuries, and sometimes even decades, it nevertheless possesses some general features which have remained unchanged throughout all epochs, and which are much less clearly marked in the styles of thought of other sciences.

The style of thought which develops in a particular discipline is not, as one might think, a merely external and therefore secondary factor, having only aesthetic value and consequently unable to influence deeply the growth of that particular branch of knowledge. On the contrary, the style of thought very much determines the precision of the subject's theoretical links, the simplicity and clarity of its scientific structure, the immediate comprehensibility of its concepts, and many other things, from which are derived in their turn the effectiveness and fruitfulness of scientific discussion and instruction in that field, and even the rate at which the subject itself develops. Among the special characteristics of the style of mathematical thought are a number of features which possess a very broad and general significance: features which, when they are adopted by a representative of some other science or by a practical worker, are often most valuable both in his own thinking and in transmitting his ideas to his pupils and followers. On reading the works of some great master in another scientific field, the mathematician often exclaims in surprise 'but he thinks in exactly the same way as we do!', his surprise arising from the fact that in this scientific field a very different style of thought is usually adopted, which has very little in common with mathematical thinking.

But if the mastery of certain features of mathematical thought can enrich the style of thought in other fields of knowledge and practical activity, making it a more powerful and productive tool, then obviously we must not neglect the use of mathematics lessons for helping young minds towards the gradual mastery of these features, so that they become firm thinking habits within the limits of mathematics itself, and later beyond them. For this purpose it is first of all necessary to try most carefully to pin down the relevant features of a mathematical style of thought. It is just this which I shall attempt to do now.

At the basis of every correctly constructed chain of argument, independent of its actual content, lies a certain formal, logical scheme, felt by the trained mind as a kind of logical skeleton, well-balanced and elegant, and covered over by the particular real content. Quite irrespective of the style of thought, this logical scheme must itself be properly constructed and free of gaps—otherwise the argument will appear inadequate and will have to be rejected.

However, the role and position of this logical skeleton may be quite different in different arguments, and may depend in an essential manner on the style of thought. In some cases the logical scheme is the determining, governing aspect of the train of thought, so that the thinker has it at all times in view, choosing and directing accordingly the successive steps in the discussion. In other cases the opposite is true, and the logical skeleton remains in the shadow, the train of thought being controlled to a much greater extent by the requirements of the factual material of the discussion; the role of logic is restricted to determining the sequence of the discussion, and even here, in a written or oral exposition of the subject, is only implied and is never refered to explicitly; as a whole, the logical scheme remains outside the thinker's field of vision. And naturally, we often meet with styles of thought which lie between these extremes.

In mathematics, the domination of the logical scheme of the discussion is taken to an extreme; a mathematician who loses sight of this scheme even for a minute forfeits the possibility of thinking accurately. This special quality of mathematical thinking, which is not encountered to such a full extent in any other science, contains much that is valuable. Clearly, it permits one to keep complete account of the accuracy of the thought-pattern, and this is a guarantee against errors. Further, it requires the thinker to keep in view every possible case in making a disjunction, binding him to take each possibility into account and to let none escape (such omissions are only too easy and in fact are often committed with other styles of thought). Thus the stylistic habits acquired in mathematics lessons, insofar as they are related to the quality we have described, have a real significance in raising the general standard of the pupils' thinking.

A very interesting and striking example of a style of thought which occurs in a field far from mathematics, but is nevertheless shot through with this quality of mathematical thinking, is afforded by the works of Marx. The reader who opens the pages of 'Capital' after studying the works of other economic writers will be struck from the very first page with the iron-hard, undeviating logic of the arguments. The implacable demands of the logical scheme not only determine the author's line of thought, but irresistably win over the reader, who is unable to escape from its controlling influence. This most unusual style for an economics writer, almost approximating to the mathematical, constantly arouses in the reader a feeling of the solidness, reliability, and extreme convincingness of what he is reading, and at the same time helps him greatly to master it.

A second characteristic feature of the mathematical style of thought which should be mentioned here is its conciseness, its conscious attempt always to find the shortest logical path leading to the given end, and its merciless rejection of everything that is not absolutely essential to achieving an impeccable logical argument. Good mathematical writing allows no digressions; extreme economy, and stern rigour of thought and exposition, make up an inalienable part of the mathematical style. This quality has considerable value, not only in mathematics, but for any form of serious discussion; laconity, the striving to exclude anything irrelevant, helps both the thinker and his reader or listener to concentrate fully on the given argument, without being distracted by side issues and without losing immediate contact with the main thread of the argument.

The leading figures of scientific thought, as a general rule, think and express themselves concisely in all fields of knowledge—even when their thoughts are founding and describing some fundamentally new idea. What a majestic impression is created, for example, by the noble economy of thought and word in the great founders of physics—Newton, Einstein, Niels Bohr! Perhaps it would be hard to find a clearer example of how great an effect on the development of a science can be attained precisely through the *style* of its founders' thought.

To a much lesser degree, this conciseness is present in great oratory. Here we often encounter prolixity, irrelevant colouration, the rejection of the straight logical path in favour of decorative images (which, of course, cannot be denied their specific force and effect). However, in this sphere also, when an orator rises and puts forward his thoughts in the compressed, economical form of extremely short, irresistibly convincing steps, majestically sacrificing for this iron logic all stylistic colouration, all temptations of picturesque image or phrase, we see how his listeners' attention at once picks up and intensifies; we feel that such a speech must arouse greater trust, and therefore carry greater influence, than many more colourful performances overladen with florid trimmings and appealing to the audience's emotions and imagination.

For mathematics, conciseness of thought is an undisputed law, sanctified by many centuries of experience. Every attempt to burden the exposition within essential (even if pleasing and intriguing), pictures discursions, or flowery passages at once gives rise to lawful suspicion and automatically calls forth an attitude of critical watchfulness. The lessons in mathematics, therefore, before those of all other disciplines, must be given the task of training the pupils in a habit of thought which is laconic, direct, admits of no distractions, and is unburdened by any superfluous elements.

A further characteristic of mathematical thought is a *clear separation* of the steps in an argument. If, for example, in proving some proposition we have to consider four possible cases, each of which further divides into a number of sub-cases, then at every stage in the discussion the mathematician is obliged to recall precisely which case and sub-case he is at present treating, and which cases and sub-cases remain to be considered. In any kind of branching argument of this sort, the mathematician must, at every moment, be able to give himself a clear account of the family of concepts of which he is at present listing the members. In everyday, non-scientific discussions we very frequently allow our classifications to get mixed up, or, miss out some elements, thereby causing confusion and mistakes in the argument. It often happens that after starting to list out all the varieties of some particular family, someone will, undetected by his listeners (and, very often, even by himself), and taking advantage of the inadequate logical precision of his argument, jump across to a different family, bringing his argument to a close with the announcement that both families have now been fully covered; yet his listeners or readers have not been told where the boundary between the members of the first and second families should be placed.

In order to render such confusions and omissions impossible, mathematics long ago adopted the extensive use of simple external methods of numeration of concepts and arguments, which are sometimes (although much less frequently) used also in other sciences. The possible cases or related concepts which have to be considered in the given discussion are listed out beforehand; similarly, within every case, all the sub-cases to be considered are listed out (sometimes, for the sake of clarity, employing some different system of numeration). Then, at the beginning of every paragraph where some new sub-case is to be considered, the number co-responding to that sub-case is set down (for example II.3—this would indicate that here the writer was about to consider the third type of the second family, if he was concerned with a classification). And the reader knows that until he meets another numbered paragraph, all the discussion relates only to this particular case and sub-case. It is clear, of course, that such a system of enumeration is purely an external aid, very useful but by no means compulsory, and that the heart of the matter lies not in this but in the clearly-marked division of the argument or classification which it both stimulates and embodies.

Finally, it is necessary to mention one other completely external tradition of the mathematical style which again, in the appropriate circumstances, can acquire educational value, and which therefore must not be neglected. I have in mind the particularly scrupulous exactitude of mathematical symbols. Every mathematical symbol possesses a strictly defined meaning. The substitution of another symbol, or a change in its position, usually brings disaster and even the complete destruction of the thought contained in a statement. The pupil not yet accustomed to sufficient exactitude in oral and written speech at first may react rather lightly to the steadfast and persistent invitation of his mathematics teacher to use absolute precision in mathematical notation. These requirements may even appear pedantic and ridiculous to him. Nevertheless, he very quickly learns from his own experience that in mathematics, non-observance of impeccable exactitude in his symbolic notation soon brings its own deserts: he loses the ability to understand the thought behind what he has written, and guesses incorrectly; either he arrives at an incorrect answer, or deprives himself generally of any possibility of resolving the problem. At best, he is able, by dint of great effort, to re-establish the correct notation and on this basis make some further progress.

Having thus been convinced that exact symbolical notation is in his own interests, the pupil then begins to watch over himself in this respect, and strict accuracy in mathematical symbolism gradually becomes a matter of habit with him. But this sort of habit, once acquired in no matter which particular field of thought, inevitably trains the pupil's general style of thought as well. He begins to express himself more exactly in both oral and written speech. In particular, he pays more attention to writing correctly, and orthographical mistakes strike him with as much force and disquiet as mathematical mistakes. We invariably notice that pupils who have been trained to be exact in their mathematical notation, more easily and quickly cease making orthographical mistakes. And I do not know whether it is possible to finish school, possessing a school-leaving certificate in mathematics, yet not having learnt to write completely correctly.

In concluding this chapter on questions concerning the educative influence of mathematics lessons on the pupil's style and culture of thought, I forsee one natural and legitimate query on the part of the reader; why have I nowhere even touched upon the problem of developing the elements of dialectical thought? I feel obliged to give a brief explanation of this point.

Marx and Engels asserted with full justification that mathematics not only provides us with the richest material for illustrating the laws of dialectical thought, but facilitates the systematic development of dialectical skills in the thinking process. However, as was frequently pointed out by the founders of Marxism, this can only fully apply to the so-called 'higher' branches of mathematics, i.e. to the mathematics of changing quantities. It is here that we first study the mathematical investigation of natural phenomena and technical processes in their living variability and not in a state of motionlessness. It is here that quantities are studied in their mutual inter-relationships (the concept of function) and not in a state of alienation from each other. Nowhere else do we see so clearly in action the change from quality to quantity, the dialectical syntheses of basically antagonistic opposites, and the other fundamental principles of dialectics. This is one of the most important reasons (although by no means the only one) compelling us to acknowledge the absolute necessity for introducing the elements of higher mathematics into the secondary school course.[1]

But, in the meantime, we can only strive for this. Of course, like every genuine and living science, the elementary mathematics taught in school is not devoid of dialectical elements. But here they are unco-ordinated and of little force, and so I have decided not to speak about them in an article concerned only with the main features of the educative influence of mathematics lessons. Nevertheless, in the very near future, I intend to write another article specifically devoted to the need to introduce the elements of higher mathematics into school education. In this article I hope to give a detailed and convincing picture of how mathematics lessons on changing quantities could be made a powerful instrument for teaching the young scholar the elements of dialectical thought.[2]

Moral Aspects and the Education of Patriotism

Very much has been said and written about the role and significance of mathematics lessons in the education of correct and disciplined thought. On the other hand, however, almost nothing has been said about the influence of mathematics studies on the formation of character and moral personality. This is very understandable: it is not usually possible for mathematical science, on account of the abstract nature of its subject-matter, to provide those directly influential, aesthetically striking and character-forming examples which are offered, for example,

[1]This hope is to some extent fulfilled in the new school programmes (B.G.).
[2]Unfortunately, this article was never written (B.G.).

by the scenes and emotions portrayed in history or literature. Nevertheless, it would be completely superficial to conclude from this that mathematics lessons should in general be completely left out of account in the process of forming a pupil's moral personality. According to my long experience, the work of mastering mathematical knowledge inevitably educates in a young person—very gradually and surreptitiously —a host of characteristics which exercise a clear moral influence and may become most important qualities of his personal make-up. But the first stage is to delve carefully into the problem of discovering precisely which features these are, and what special qualities of mathematical work may be capable of developing them.

Honesty and Truthfulness

In all types of everyday lawsuits, each of the opposing parties is concerned as a rule to bring about the desired, favourable decision of the dispute. With varying degrees of ingenuity, therefore, each seeks to discover the most convincing arguments to obtain a favourable decision. Depending on the epoch, and the cirumstances and content of the quarrel, the parties appeal to this or that higher authority, be it general morality, 'natural' law, holy writings, juridical codes, working rules of inner conduct or, very often, the statements of different authoritative scholars or acknowledged political leaders. All of us have many times noticed the earnestness of such quarrels, and the conviction which obviously lies in the pleadings of both parties. One might think that the litigant really wished to arrive at a true and just decision, consonant with the spirit and letter of the particular authoritative sources acknowledged as arbiter in the matter.

But it is well-known that a similar picture is presented by many other disputes. Precisely those same features appear very often even in scientific discussion. Conclusions made by one scholar with full conviction are called into question by another with the same degree of conviction. Soon a polemic arises, in which each of the parties finds even further arguments to support his position. Often, even repeated experiments suggest to each of the disputants the very thing that he wishes to prove. In the course of the debate, each of the parties not only strives to strengthen his own position, but endeavours, by various means, to discredit the stand taken by his opponent, sometimes even to the extent of attempting to discredit his personality. It is only comparatively seldom, in such a prolonged polemic, that one of the contestants finds the honesty and manliness to acknowledge the falsity of his position.

The subjective reasons for this phenomenon in scientific life are easily understandable; in no way, unfortunately, do they differ from the subjective reasons for the most petty, everyday quarrels. Nor is it difficult to find objective reasons for the possibility of scientific situations of this type; in the empirical sciences, each new, as yet incompletely established, law is at least temporarily regarded as a 'working hypothesis'; wherever the question is not conclusively resolved there are usually considerations (experimental or theoretical) speaking in favour of the hypothesis, as there are others speaking against it. Of two scholars, one may attempt to resolve the problem by gathering together as many arguments as possible which support the hypothesis, and the other may be concerned with collecting facts and considerations capable of calling the hypothesis into disrepute. The process is conducted in the same way as a criminal action, where the tasks facing the prosecuting and defending counsels are to bring into order and set out all the arguments respectively for and against the guilt of the defendant.

Up to this stage, of course, a scientific discussion arranged in this way does not contain in itself anything morally repugnant. The gathering together of all possible relevant arguments for and against a 'working hypothesis' has always been of benefit to scientific progress. Obviously there is nothing reprehensible in the fact that the arguments for and against the hypothesis have been gathered together by two different scholars or groups of scholars, provided that both sides approach the problem honestly and are governed exclusively by a wish to further the search for objective truth. Moral odium and ethical censure begin when a scholar's conclusions cease to be governed by the interests of objective truth and—consciously, half-consciously, or unconsciously—start to serve his own personal interests—his stubbornness, his honour, his self-esteem; when the discussion starts to be conducted emotionally, when arguments are dragged in 'by the scruff of their necks' and are unobjectively accentuated, exactly as in everyday squabbles. Such degradation of a scientific dispute is sometimes a dark spot on even the greatest representatives of scientific thought.

Only mathematical science is able to avoid this fully. It knows no 'working hypotheses'—propositions whose truth is open to discussion. Until a proposition is proved, it cannot, in general, be admitted to the treasure-house of science, and no-one would think of upholding it. But once it is proved, then its truth must be acknowledged by all and can in no way be subject to doubt. No intermediate positions are known in mathematics. For example, only an ignoramus, a charlatan, or a mentally ill person (and all three categories are from time to time encountered—one has only to recall the 'Fermatists', or the knights of the squared circle and the trisected angle) would engage in a polemic in defence of an invalid proof. Such a 'defence' would immediately, unanimously and mercilessly be exposed by the scientific world. No amount of emotional or tendentious argumentation, no far-fetched allusions could ever have the slightest success in mathematics. Of course, this concerns only the actual subject-matter of mathematics itself; on questions of the logical or philosophical foundations of mathematics, disputes are quite possible and indeed inevitable; so are questions of a personal nature related to the advance of mathematics (for example, questions of priority).

Every mathematician soon becomes accustomed to the fact that in his science, any attempt for some reason to act tendentiously, any bias in favour of this or that solution of the question, causing him to listen only to arguments speaking in favour of the chosen solution, is a certain route to failure, and will only bring him disappointment. Here, the state of affairs where an incorrect or not fully correct argument could turn out to the advantage of the arguer, is in principle impossible. Hence the mathematician quickly grows accustomed to the fact that in his science only accurate, objective reasoning, free of any tendentious argumentation, will be of value to him, and that success will only come from unprejudiced, unbiased application of his mind. And independently of his general moral standards, in his scientific work he will never be governed except by considerations of objective truth.

But this quality, developing naturally in the mathematics specialist, will be acquired to some extent by every non-specialist who studies mathematics, and, in particular, by every school-child. The school-child knows very well that it is impossible to 'throw dust in the eyes' of the mathematics teacher, that no amount of aplomb or eloquence will help him pass off ignorance for knowledge, or an invalid argument for a valid one. And no matter how untruthful he might be in other matters, in mathematics he takes care to avoid false assertions and invalid proofs.

But here also, as is often the case, moral habits acquired in some particular field, carry over to some extent to other spheres of thought and practical activity. Honesty of thought, having become for the mathematician an inexorable law of his scientific thinking and professional (in particular teaching) activities, influences him in all aspects of his life—from abstract discussions to every-day behaviour.

I must admit that I myself am organically incapable of admitting some assertion (even of an everyday, practical nature) unless I am in possession of a proof admitting no objections. The professional habit of absolute objectivity in argumentation will not permit me, under any circumstances, to brazenly insist (as many others would) on some personally favourable solution. In this way, the quality of which I have spoken may sometimes even prove of danger to its possessor. But nevertheless I value it highly, and I am glad to have it. I am also glad whenever I notice it in others, because I hold it to be of no small moral worth.

I have always been interested in this quality, and have many times observed how much it develops in people under the influence of serious scientific intercourse—in particular, under the stimulus of mathematics lessons. It is a very joyous and morally uplifting picture to see a person gradually overcoming in himself disgusting or stupid habits—subjecting his selfish, petty, mercenary interests to the general laws of thought; ceasing to defend in theory only those aspects which would be advantageous to him in practice; learning to value objective accuracy as a high spiritual and cultural achievement, and ever more often and with lighter heart sacrificing for its sake his own personal interests. Taken to an extreme, this quality reveals itself as none other than honesty and truthfulness—one of the finest ornaments of a person's moral character.

Persistence and Manliness

Conscientious and serious work on building up and consolidating knowledge in any scientific field demands a systematic concentration of mental effort, persistence in overcoming difficulties, a manly encounter with disappointment. For this reason, work of this type, given proper supervision, inevitably develops in the pupil corresponding qualities of character—industry, perseverance, persistence in following his aims, the ability not to give up in the face of difficulties or to become disheartened as a result of failure. It is immediately clear how decisive an influence such qualities may have in the growth of a morally and socially full-valued human individual, and how much attention the teacher ought therefore to give towards making the maximum use of his lessons for inculcating these qualities. The different subjects of the school programme present very numerous and varied opportunities in this direction. There is no subject which does not have among its specific features some which are of key value in this educational process. Our problem here is naturally to indicate those characteristics of mathematics which distinguish it from the other school disciplines in developing the school-child's intelligent determination and conscious manliness—two inestimable qualities of the future warrior.

First of all, I would like to single out here the clearly defined aim of any mathematical task, its desired and stipulated end. If the task is the composition of a historical or literary essay, it is impossible to indicate a stage at which this task can be considered finally accomplished —the possibilities of adding and perfecting, of making systematic improvements of every kind, are here almost unlimited. On the other hand, the pupil will not feel himself competent to make an authoritative assessment of his own work: what appears successful to him in the essay, may meet with quite a different reception from the teacher. All this uncertainty and vagueness in assessing the quality and level of perfection of his work, inevitable as it is from the nature of the task, will certainly have an enfeebling influence on the will to work of an as yet relatively unschooled mind. But if the task consists in the solution of a problem or the proof of a theorem, this in itself is enough to indicate quite definitely when the task can be considered fully accomplished: as soon as the problem is solved or the theorem proved. All the rest—setting out the formal solution, use of accurate notation, etc. —has a secondary, not a determining value in the eyes of both the teacher and the pupil. Equally, the quality of the work can be assessed with unambiguous precision; the problem must be *truly* solved, and the theorem must be *correctly* proved. To check his argument for the absence of logical errors is something the pupil can and must learn to do for himself; in the case of a problem he may even know specific methods of verifying the solution. It is easy to understand what a stimulating influence on his persistence and determination in achieving his aims such a clear-cut indication of the result can and does present. Victory here is as immediately perceptible as in a game of chess or a sporting contest, and the pupil can just as surely evaluate his achievements as the competent teacher.

The second, considerably deeper and more important quality of mathematics exercises that I would like to mention here is the *creative* element which, in the great majority of cases, they contain. Where in most fields of knowledge, the fulfilment of the task demands, with few exceptions, only a certain amount of given knowledge and skill, or at best the ability to set out this knowledge elegantly and stylistically correctly, the solution of a mathematical problem demands as a rule the creation of a special argument to attain the stated aim, and in this way becomes an—albeit quite modest—creative art. It is just this creative, research character of mathematics exercises which, more than any other factor, attracts to mathematics the young powers of the pupil's growing and strengthening intellect. No one who has once felt the exciting glow of creative achievement will spare any effort to experience it again. No difficulties will deter him; the strength of his struggles and attempts, his perseverance and ability to withstand set-backs, will grow with every new achievement. He will learn to meet with failures, mistakes, periods of confusion and bewilderment, as befits a true warrior—not yielding to them, but finding in them the source and stimulus for ever further efforts of mind and will.

The Development of Patriotism

The problem of using mathematics lessons for developing and strengthening the pupil's feeling of pride in and love for his homeland presents a specific difficulty, the obvious cause of which is rooted in the abstract character of mathematical science. It is necessary to say straight out that on account of this difficulty, mathematics cannot directly, through its own material or content, serve as an instrument of propaganda for any such concrete cause as the beauty or greatness of the homeland. Here it must, with due modesty, give pride of place to other subjects.

However, during his lessons in mathematics the pupil is by no means solely occupied with the abstract essence of his subject. In every lesson, the abstract themes of mathematics are continually implemented, supplemented and illustrated by a very wide range of different concrete material; into this category come the contextual material of the text-book problems, historical references, different types of application, and so on. In many cases, the choice of contextual material can be varied within wide limits and to a significant extent is therefore at the disposal of the teacher. Evidently, the teacher can make wide use of this freedom in order to direct the pupils' attention to facts and figures which will support and develop their love for the mother-country. Several writers have already suggested that the choice of material for text-book problems should be given a patriotic basis. No objections can be raised against this argument; it is necessary only to give very careful thought to the choice of material for this purpose, in order to avoid cheapening or vulgarizing the patriotic motive—as can happen if the factual content of the problem is unnatural, 'dragged in by the scruff of its neck', or if the facts and figures, however interesting in themselves, are included in a problem that has neither immediate interest nor practical application. At the same time it is necessary to realize quite clearly that this is a purely exterior approach to the question, for it is not mathematics as such which is being used to develop patriotic feelings, but the mathematics lessons.

Much more closely connected with mathematics itself is the approach that consists in giving a patriotic orientation to a whole series of historical facts. This approach, as well as being impressively effective in action, is of particular value in that it greatly heightens the pupils' interest in the history of mathematics, and in many cases provides the possibility of and an opportunity for acquainting the pupils with mathematical facts lying outside the official syllabus and augmenting it in a particularly happy manner. Since this question has remained almost untreated in our country, I shall pause here to consider it in somewhat more detail.

The history of Russian and Soviet mathematics is rich in facts which, especially if considered against the correct historical background, are capable of arousing in us a happy feeling of legitimate pride. Many of these facts would be sufficiently within the grasp of secondary school children for them to appreciate their principal significance and practical value. Here it is necessary only that the teacher himself should be well informed both as to the facts themselves and their role in mathematics and science, and as to the historical background against which these concepts arose and developed. It is also necessary, of course, to be able to describe these facts to the school-children in such a way as to awaken their lively interest in the subject and to extract maximum effect from the point of view both of the pupils' mathematical development, and of instilling in them a healthy feeling of national pride.

It is well known how very suitable for all these ends is the tale of the history and fate of the scientific ideas of our great fellow countrymen N. I. Lobachevski. In essentials, Lobachevski's great geometrical thought is well within the range of schoolchildren in the upper classes, and a properly conducted discussion on this theme could help greatly, on the one hand, in understanding the idea of the axiomatic approach so basic for modern mathematics, and, on the other hand, in instilling a deep respect for both the scientific genius of Lobachevski, and his extraordinary steadfastness—that tremendous strength of conviction which enabled him to create his theory in isolation, without social recognition, in a scientifically hostile atmosphere.

Much less familiar here are the achievements of another of our great scholars P. L. Chebyshev. Yet his scientific image is no less imposing than Lobachevski's. There would be much of value, from many points of view, in telling the schoolchildren something about him also. Chebyshev was among the number of those few scholars of the very highest rank, who, during their life, work in many, sometimes quite widely separated fields of mathematics, in each of them laying down completely new paths which their successors will continue to tread for many years to come. The great spirit of innovation was Chebyshev's possession no less than Lobachevski's. In the theory of numbers, the theory of probability, the theory of mechanisms, and the theory of approximations he created powerful new methods and became one of the founders of many scientific schools, both within Russia and beyond its borders. His great ideas are by no means exhausted even today.

Chebyshev's achievements in the theory of numbers are particularly well suited and instructive for the pupils of secondary schools. Euclid's theorem on the existence of an infinite number of primes is known to everyone. It would be particularly useful to draw up a table of prime numbers, anyhow up to 100, and call the pupils' attention to the obvious absence of any regularity in their distribution. Then the teacher could describe how the problem of finding regularities in the sequence of prime numbers has been, and remains, one of the central problems of arithmetic. It would be worthwhile mentioning (without proof) the theorem of Euler that $\pi(n)/n \to 0$ as $n \to \infty$, a result that should be quite comprehensible to the school-children and well able to arouse their interest. Then it would be possible to touch—in the most general terms—on Chebyshev's asymptotic results, making sure to give the historical picture of the great efforts that had been devoted to this problem before Chebyshev. As a concrete example, it would be particularly valuable to pause at the (quite elementary) Bertrand's conjecture[1] and verify it for a series of examples, in this way stimulating the pupil's interest. Later on it might be possible to consider one or other of its elementary proofs, perhaps in the form of a problem for the mathematical circles.

I would strongly advise directing the pupils' attention to the following remarkable historical fact. Arithmetic and geometry are the two most ancient and most important sections of mathematics, and in each of these, over a very long period, mathematicians were largely nourished on the works of Euclid. For many centuries, the central problems of these two fundamental branches of mathematics—the theory of parallels in geometry and the problem of the distribution of the primes in arithmetic—did not yield significantly to the countless attempts of whole generations of mathematicians to solve them. And then, in the nineteenth century, both problems were finally brought to the brink of defeat. In geometry, this was achieved by the Russian mathematician Lobachevski, and in arithmetic by the Russian mathematician Chebyshev. Both of these, each in his respective field, laid down paths along which mathematics is still successfully developing to the present day. There can be no doubt that these great historical leaps—Euclid-Lobachevski and Euclid-Chebyshev—must make a considerable impression on young minds already able to understand much of their significance.

Having interested the pupils in questions concerning the distribution of primes, the teacher has a very natural excuse for telling them something about the celebrated Goldbach conjecture[2]. It would be very worthwhile verifying this conjecture at least for numbers up to 100. Then he could mention (without proofs, of course) the outstanding discoveries of the Soviet mathematician Academician I. M. Vinogradov, whose fundamental result concerning the Goldbach problem should be well within the pupils' grasp.

Conclusion

I have deliberately left completely to one side the question, most important for the theme of the present discussion, of the significance of mathematics lessons in forming the pupil's world-view. I have done this for the same reason that in the first chapter I refused to consider the question of using mathematics lessons for developing the skills of dialectical thinking: although familiarity with the ideas and methods

[1]There is at least one prime between x and $2x - 2$, if $x \geqslant 4$ (trans.).
[2]Every even number $N \geqslant 6$ is the sum of two odd primes (trans.).

of mathematics has a fundamental importance in forming a world-view, the lion's portion of its educative effect in this direction belongs to the mathematics of variable quantities, to the so-called higher mathematics. It is here, according to Engels, that dialectics enters mathematics; but unfortunately almost the whole of this part of mathematics still remains outside the boundaries of our school programme. In such circumstances, there is really little point in discussing the educative effect of the dialectically arid portion of mathematics which is sheltered under our present system of school teaching. One could say a good deal about the powerful strides towards forming and directing a world-view which can and in practice often do result from the study of higher mathematics. However, I intend to leave the discussion of these questions to the article already mentioned in the second chapter.

In the present article, I have not considered any methodological questions. I have said something about *which* characteristic features of mathematics can and should be used to develop *which* particular intellectual or moral qualities in the student, but nowhere have I touched on the question of *how* this should be done. My experience tells me that this circumstance may cause dissatisfaction among a certain portion of my readers, and doubtless I am not guaranteed against nerve-grating reproaches that my article 'has nothing in it for the teacher', advice to 'have a look around me', and so on.

I therefore feel myself obliged to give the following brief explanation on this point.

(1) I think that it is quite unnecessary to put together any detailed methodological instructions relating to the questions I have considered in this article. Lessons in mathematics (as in any other subject) are only capable of having even the slightest educative influence on the conditions that, firstly, the teacher has a thorough knowledge of his subject, including its history and methods of teaching; secondly, he possesses an adequate amount of teaching experience and tact; and finally, he himself exhibits to a sufficient degree all those qualities he is hoping to instil in his pupils. No methodological cribs can help the teacher train his pupils to think clearly if he is unable to think clearly himself. Or again, what possible methodological system can help the teacher make his pupils ardent patriots if he himself has only a lukewarm, indifferent feeling towards his mother country?

And conversely, if the teacher is on top of his task, if he possesses in full measure all those qualities that we listed above, then he will not have the slightest need for any methodological hints on these problems. In any particular case, he will find for himself, easily and unforcedly, the most effective route to the desired end. It would be an insult to his work to tie him down to a fixed, concrete approach.

(2) Although I consider in this way that it would be futile in practice

to give any detailed methodological instructions on the questions I have discussed, it seems to me that it might nevertheless be of some value to give one or two *general* methodological hints. I think it would be a very good thing if my article was to provoke one or two of our best teachers and methodologists into putting forward their opinions on this question, and sharing the conclusions of their experience with their younger colleagues. Since they are, in any case, more competent than I, with due modesty I shall leave this question to them.

Finally, I should like to try and protect myself in advance from one type of criticism which I foresee, and which is often based on a mis-understanding. Because I have been speaking of the educative effect of mathematics lessons, I have, quite naturally, listed out one after the other just those features of mathematics which give it some particular advantages over other disciplines in this respect. This was precisely my task. But whenever one starts off in this fashion, it appears to the thoughtless reader that one has set out to elevate mathematics over all other disciplines, and that one's whole article is baldly asserting that mathematics is the only true science, that all other disciplines suffer from this or the other defect, and can only be called sciences with a certain reservation. My respected colleagues—representatives of the other sciences—begin to feel themselves unjustly attacked, and present their work for open scrutiny, to show that other sciences are not one jot worse than mathematics, and that all those advantages I have claimed for mathematics are in point of fact divided equally among all other disciplines.

With the first point of this criticism I am in thorough and whole-hearted agreement—other sciences are most definitely in no way worse than mathematics. More than this, I have the very deepest respect for those representatives of other sciences who are capable of making discoveries of great value in fields where, in my view, creative work is a good deal harder than in mathematics. But then, never once in my article have I claimed that mathematics is the highest of the sciences. On the contrary, I have several times pointed out with all modesty, that, for the given purpose, mathematics is above all characterized by a purely negative feature—it is abstract, its subject-matter is not taken from the objects and phenomena of the real world itself, but only from their quantitative relations and spatial patterns. This circumstance, as I have several times emphasized, makes the educational problem in mathematics considerably more difficult than in many other school disciplines. But at the same time, mathematics does possess some features which, in certain respects, give it greater educational possi-bilities than other disciplines. And the fact that in this article I have concentrated attention on just these features in no way implies that I wish to claim for mathematics an unduly prominent role, or to raise it above all other sciences.

I give mathematics only what is hers by right, openly recognizing those other qualities which in the given context make up her weakness. But for those advantages which I have attributed to her, I am prepared to hold out to the end. And if respected colleagues wish to assert that some concrete feature, which I have asserted is the monopoly or the prerogative of mathematics, is in fact found to an equal degree in all other sciences, then on such a point, wherever and whenever is convenient, I am ready to back up my opinion, in the full conviction that I can win my case before any competent and unbiased judge.

APPENDIX 1

A. YA. KHINCHIN: A BIOGRAPHICAL SKETCH

These notes represent a condensed version of the two articles appearing at the end of the Russian edition of 'Pedagogical Essays': 'Alexander Yakovlevich Khinchin' by B. V. Gnedenko; 'A. Ya Khinchin as a teacher of Mathematical Analysis' by A. I. Markushevich. Since a rather complete account of Khinchin's mathematical work has already appeared in English (in B.V. Gnedenko's memorial address to the Fourth Berkeley Symposium, California, 1960), together with a complete list of his published works, we have concentrated here on those details that concern his teaching activities, giving only a brief outline of his scientific interests. Some further remarks and quotations will be found in the second Appendix.

Of Khinchin's early life, Gnedenko writes as follows:

"Alexander Yakovlevich Khinchin was born on the 19th July, 1894, in the village of Kondrova in the Medynsky county of Kaluga Province, known at that time for its paper factory. His father was chief engineer in the paper mill, a well-known and respected figure among the specialists of the paper-making industry. Khinchin spent his early childhood in Kondrova, as well as his holidays when he was a student at the real-school, and later at the University, in Moscow. Khinchin had a lively, sociable character and made friends with his contemporaries among the young factory workers. His comrades developed a passion for the theatre. Their enthusiasm was so great that they created their own amateur theatre in Kondrova. I can remember Khinchin telling me that he himself took part both as producer and as actor. Occasionally they would charge for their shows, and with the money thus earned organize trips to Moscow to see performances of the Moscow Arts Theatre.

At the same time these years of his early youth were the years of his entrancement with literature, which had as their result the publication of several small volumes of verse in the years 1912–17. Literary interests long struggled in him with mathematical interests. His love for mathematics finally conquered only in the last class of the real-school, when he became acquainted with the ideas of mathematical analysis. His final choice was strongly influenced by the fact that his teacher in the real-school was one of the best school mathematicians, M. F. Berg, whose text-book at that time enjoyed wide popularity. There can be no doubt that his love for the theatre and literature had a strong influence not only in moulding Alexander Yakovlevich's qualities as a citizen, but also in contributing to his development as one of the most brilliant lecturers and mathematical writers. Orally, as well as in writing, he was able to combine in the most masterful way a superb literary style with scientific depth, rigour, and exceptional clarity and precision. I remember that one could attend his lectures at meetings of the Moscow Mathematical Society without fear, because all the details of the proof and the basic idea that he wished to describe would be clear even if one had never studied the particular problems of which Khinchin was talking.

In 1911, after finishing the real-school, Khinchin entered the Faculty of Mathematics and Physics in Moscow University. At that time Professors D. F. Egorov and N. N. Lusin had started work on the theory of functions of a real variable, and had already obtained some fundamental results in this field. Many students were attracted to this study, and enthusiastically started work under the supervision of D. F. Egorov and N. N. Lusin. Among their number was A. Ya. Khinchin. His first independent scientific step was suggested by A. Denjoy's work on primitive functions. In a paper read to the student mathematics circle on 6th November, 1914, Khinchin put forward a generalization of the idea of derivative that was well in keeping with the whole spirit of the metric theory of functions, and which has now passed into the arsenal of modern mathematics under the name of asymptotic derivative.

At the same time Khinchin was working successfully in other branches of mathematics. This we can judge if only from the proclamation of the Professorial Council[1] 25.XI.1915, section 30 of which reads: "The gold medal shall be awarded to student Khinchin for his essay entitled 'Infinite series of functions and their convergence, term-by-term integration and differentiation' ".

Alexander Yakovlevich's talents were soon recognized by the University, and after finishing the University course in 1916 he was selected for further training towards the title of Professor. His teaching work started in 1918 at the Moscow Polytechnic Institute for Women. One year later he was invited to take the post of professor in the Polytechnic Institute that had recently been organized by M. V. Frunze in Ivanovo-Voznesensky. Soon afterwards the Ivanovo-Voznesensky Pedagogical Institute was formed, and Khinchin was elected dean of the Faculty of Mathematics and Physics. He gave much attention to student entry, to organizing the teaching programme, and to popularizing scientific knowledge. His public lectures on varied themes—mathematics, psychology, literature—enjoyed tremendous popularity. This was enthusiastically recounted to me at Ivanovo-Voznesensky in the 1930's, by many of those who had struggled hard to avoid missing any of Alexander Yakovlevich's public lectures.

In 1922 the Research Institute in Mathematics and Mechanics was founded at Moscow University. From the moment of its inception, Khinchin was invited to become one of the scientific workers. For some time he combined this work with his work in Ivanovo-Voznesensky. Later he became Head of the Mathematics Department in the Liebknecht Pedagogical Institute. Then in 1927 he obtained a professorship at Moscow University, and returned to work there for good. From that time on his activities were indissolubly linked with the University: he was Head of the Department of Probability Theory, later Head of the Department of Mathematical Analysis, and (1932–34) Director of the Moscow University Research Institute in Mathematics and Mechanics. In Moscow University Khinchin deservedly enjoyed the reputation of one of the most outstanding lecturers. Indeed, his lectures were distinguished not only by their high scientific quality, but by their literary perfection, their exceptional ease of understanding, and the elegance of their exposition. It is no wonder that his lectures attracted large audiences. Many mathematicians in the Soviet Union are happy to consider themselves his pupils and to carry out in practice his scientific and methodological principles. I also am happy, in that it was my good fortune to become one of the closest, if not the very closest, of his students. I shall always carry in my memory the warmth of his feelings towards other people, and his constant desire to be of real assistance to anyone who was working and deserved success."

[1]Ucheny sov'et.

Gnedenko at this stage goes on to describe Khinchin's scientific achievements. We shall limit ourselves here to some very brief comments. To summarize the overall influence and directions of Khinchin's scientific work we shall quote from the opening paragraphs of Gnedenko's address to the Berkeley Symposium. After outlining the ever-growing role of statistical concepts in physics, chemistry, biology, economics and other sciences, and commenting on the relatively backward state of probability theory even during the first two decades of this century, Gnedenko continues:

". . . Consequently, one of the most urgent problems of the second decade of this century was the problem of transforming the theory of probability into a well-organized mathematical discipline with logically clear-cut fundamental concepts, with widely developed specific methods of investigation, and with distinctly established connections with other branches of mathematics. In order that the theory of probability should become a real tool in scientific research, the field of probabilistic problems had to be broadened, and this broadening required a deep analysis of the peculiarities of mathematical formulations of the problems of science.

The role which A. Ya. Khinchin played in the solution of the whole complex of the above problems is exceptionally large. And, in spite of their diversity, his scientific interests impress by their internal unity and by their scientific coherence. In general terms, they can be characterized as a systematic study of the place and significance of statistical laws in various parts of mathematics, in the natural sciences, and in technology."

Thus Khinchin's main field of scientific work must be regarded as the theory of probability; indeed, with A. N. Kolmogorov he can be regarded as one of the founders of the whole modern Soviet School of Probability Theory, which dates roughly from 1927 when he first took up the chair at Moscow University. His own name is linked with fundamental contributions concerning the law of the iterated logarithm (1924), the law of large numbers (1929) and, perhaps outstanding among his works on the basic theory, the theory of limit distributions of sums of independent random variables (1927, 1933, 1937), and the theory of stationary processes (1933–34). As early as 1929, he became interested in the problems of statistical physics, and grew to the conviction that the fundamental mathematical problems of statistical physics could be reduced to problems in the theory of probability, and in particular to the theory of limit theorems for sums of independent random variables. These ideas found expression in his several monographs on statistical physics (1943, 1950, 1951) and led also to the development of local limit theorems for sums of random variables. The final phase of his work in probability theory concerns the theory of mass service (or the theory of queues) (1956) and information theory (1953, 1956).

But although we may choose probability theory as his main field of scientific interest, his work in this field was closely linked to his interests in other mathematical disciplines. We have already seen how his first papers were concerned with problems of the theory of functions of a real variable and measure theory. This led to an interest in the metric theory of numbers and from there to his early papers on probability theory. He returned many times to real variable and number theory, especially to those areas where they share common ground with probability theory, writing many research papers as well as a number of delightful popular accounts (for example, his books on continued fractions, elementary probability theory and the 'Three Pearls of Number Theory'). He was also the author of two outstanding textbooks on mathematical analysis, which are described in the article by Professor Markushevich.

These few remarks will have to suffice as an account of his scientific achievements. We include at the end of this Appendix a list of his books, including their English translations, where available, and of his writings on philosophical and teaching questions. For fuller accounts of his scientific work, and for a complete list of his publications, we refer the reader to Gnedenko's Berkeley address quoted earlier, and to the biographical articles which appeared at the time of Khinchin's death,[1] and earlier on the occasion of his 60th birthday,[2] in the Uspekhi Matematicheskikh Nauk.

We come now to our main theme, Khinchin's interest in and work on the problems of mathematics teaching in the schools and institutes of higher education. From his very earliest days, Khinchin must have felt a strong urge to the art of teaching, to helping others to understand and appreciate ideas with whose importance or elegance he himself was impressed. Gnedenko and Kolmogorov remark[3] that 'in life he was able to combine harmoniously creative ability, which developed along lines of complete originality and rare depth, with the study of the achievements of others and the art of systematizing and popularizing the results of scientific research'. At the same time he was not content with the passive role of an author, but sought active participation in the application, organization and implementation of his ideas. Let us return now to Gnedenko's main narrative.

'Our portrait of the scholar would be very seriously dimmed if we did not add to it one further feature: his constant interest in the problems of teaching, both in the institutes of higher education and in the secondary schools. His views on teaching were set out in text books, monographs, popular books, special articles and book reviews. On many occasions he appeared in front of an audience of teachers with papers on the most vital methodological, educational and general pedagogical problems—at meetings of the Teaching and Methodological Council of the RSFSR Narkompros,[4] the Mathematics Department of the Scientific

[1]Uspekhi Mat. Nauk, XV(1960), pp. 97–110.
[2]Uspekhi Mat. Nauk, X(1955).
[3]In the obituary notice referred to above.
[4]Uchebno-metodicheski sov'et Narkomprosa RSFSR.

Research Institute for the Schools of the RSFSR Narkompros,[1] and later in the Academy of Pedagogical Sciences of the RSFSR.

In the period 1938–40 Alexander Yakovlevich was director of the physics and mathematics section of the Teaching and Methodological Council of the RSFSR Narkompros, and the Mathematics Department of the Scientific Research Institute for the Schools of the RSFSR Narkompros. Later, from the moment of inception of the Academy of Pedagogical Sciences of the RSFSR, he became one of their full members, and was elected a member of the Presidium. He took a lively and active part in its work, inducing qualified specialists—mathematicians and methodologists—to co-operate in its work, discussing and putting into action plans for its publishing activities, organizing and carrying out "Readings for Teachers". Nor should one pass over in silence Khinchin's work in organizing the writers who contributed to the mathematical reference book "An Encyclopedia of Elementary Mathematics". As is well known, his role in the preparation of these volumes was not only that of editor; he was also author of the excellent article "Elements of Number Theory".[2]

The fate of mathematics teaching in Soviet secondary schools was a subject that always deeply concerned Alexander Yakovlevich. Noticing some shortcomings in school mathematics teaching, he did not consider it possible to rest content with unremitting criticism of these weaknesses, but always attempted to take active steps to help in their eradication. As long ago as 1938 he presented long papers on these questions to the Moscow Mathematical Society, and later, in 1943, to the Professorial Council of the Steklov Mathematical Institute. At the same time he prepared extensive notes to accompany his lectures, which were later passed on to the RSFSR Narkompros. These notes revealed many shortcomings in the syllabuses, in the text-books, in teacher training courses, and suggested important measures to remedy them. They are still not out-of-date, and may be considered as having become in a certain sense syllabus documents.

Alexander Yakovlevich's basic methodological principles found their fullest expression in two of his works:[3] the brochure "Basic Mathematical Concepts and Mathematical Definitions in the Secondary Schools", and his book "Eight Lectures on Mathematical Analysis". In somewhat abbreviated form, these principles can be set out as follows:

1. Mathematical knowledge must always be taught in accordance with its treatment in modern mathematics. It may sometimes be necessary, taking into account the child's age, to give these ideas in a somewhat simplified form, but the treatment such ideas are given in school should never falsify the scientific treatment by including features that contradict the scientific picture of the idea.

2. The substitution of precise, exact definitions, formulations and arguments by vague ones having no precise meaning and leading in further use to logical absurdities can in no circumstances simplify the understanding of some concept: "thinking in foggy terms can never be easier than thinking in precise terms".

3. The usual structure of the school course is overburdened with concepts that are unknown in mathematical science or were long ago abandoned by it. In the great majority of cases, the introduction of ideas of this type, that have been thought up specially for school-teaching and are unknown to mathematics, has nothing in its favour save blind tradition; to burden the course with such concepts will bring no teaching advantages and will only cause harm.

4. Teaching must not suppress the pupil's creative abilities, but must assist him

[1]Kabinet Matermatiki Nauchno-issledovatel'skogo instituta shkol Narkomprosa RSFSR.
[2]Reference (140) in the bibliography at the end of the appendix.
[3]References (104) and (116).

in developing initiative in seeking methods of proof and in solving problems.

5. The teacher need not descend to the tiniest details nor strive for absolute completeness in describing points of second-order importance. At the same time, he has no cause to regret time spent in illustrating and illuminating some concept, method or idea that has a leading, fundamental significance, nor to spare any efforts, by making use of the most varied descriptions and visual images, to lodge the basic ideas fully and firmly in the minds of his listeners or readers.

Such an approach provides the opportunity for developing the pupil's ability to distinguish, in his later, independent work, between essential aspects and those that have only a secondary, minor significance.

How often do we hear that in the details of the course, the pupils lose sight of the overall picture and of the contents and significance of their science—that they lose sight of the wood for the trees? Yet at the same time we all know "how useful it is to sometimes turn away from the trees and take a look at the wood".

Anyone who has even once heard Alexander Yakovlevich give a full lecture course, or even a scientific paper, will remember the exceptional care of formulation, the exceptional attention he paid to describing the place of his subject in the system of mathematical knowledge. And involuntarily the listener would forget that a moment before these ideas were unfamiliar to him. He would start to feel the importance and value of the subject Khinchin was discussing, and soon would no longer be in a position where he was capable of losing the underlying ideas, the thread of the argument, or the particular features of the chosen approach. The listener would start to live his role. He would experience pleasure at the fact that he had been enabled to reach a step higher on the ladder of scientific understanding, to grapple with the complex interactions of concepts, ideas and methods. In this, perhaps, at least to some extent, lay A. Ya. Khinchin's success as a teacher and as the originator of new lines of research in probability theory, the theory of numbers, the theory of functions of a real variable, and in teaching methods.

In his private life, Khinchin was very exacting of himself. He gave a great deal of attention to the scientific development of his students, encouraging every sign of intelligent initiative. I am happy that as a postgraduate student and later in our joint work I had the opportunity of seeing him both at work and at home. His favourite recreation was a walk in the woods. But even then he did not cease to think of his favourite subject. Thus, I can remember how in the summer months of 1936 and 1937, when we were walking together, he would raise many interesting ideas and questions concerning the arithmetic of distributions. At that time also we spoke of many problems of teaching.

He could not tolerate unfinished business, and never allowed himself to put on the shoulders of others work for which he was responsible. Alexander Yakovlevich did not aspire to outside honours. Although he was a scholar of world renown, a corresponding member of the Academy of Sciences of the USSR, and Academician and a member of the Presidium of the Academy of Pedagogical Sciences of the RSFSR, he continued to lead a modest life, valuing people for their inner qualities and not for their positions. He sincerely welcomed every major scientific advance, and the appearance of every new gifted student. I remember his pride in V. V. Stepanova's brilliant young student M. V. Bebutov, and in the appearance of a talented new representative of probability theory in France—W. Doeblin—and how he suffered at their untimely deaths.[1]

On 18th October, 1959 Khinchin died after a long and painful illness. Soviet mathematics has suffered a great loss.'

[1]M. V. Bebutov was killed at the front in 1941; W. Doeblin was executed on 22nd June, 1940 for offering armed resistance to Hitler's forces. (B.G.).

We shall conclude this biographical sketch with Professor Markushevich's account of Khinchin's achievements in teaching analysis.

"A. Ya. Khinchin as a Teacher of Mathematical Analysis

A. Ya. Khinchin happily combined the erudition, depth and creative temperament of a great scholar with a wonderful mastery of teaching.

He delivered his lectures smoothly, unhurriedly, in a quiet but very precise and somehow penetrating voice. His lecture courses were not over-large in content, and were free from distracting details. But he never regretted time spent on illustrating clearly the importance and significance of a mathematical concept, or on motivating the formulation of a question or problem. Such psychological preparation of his listeners for the absorption of new material was an unchanging part of his style of exposition, and it was in this, perhaps, rather than in the other peculiarities of his style, that the master-teacher showed himself. By this means he was able to prepare the auditorium for the mental tasks that lay before it. Only under such conditions can one expect that the listeners will appreciate the significance of the stated problem, will consciously await the lecturer's supervision, and will follow him through all the steps of a complicated mathematical construction without feeling either indifference or boredom. And indeed, there was no place for passivity in the room where Khinchin was lecturing. The lecturer watched keenly over the students, making sure that his line of argument had been followed by all those making an honest attempt to listen and to think. But kindly Alexander Yakovlevich would frown sternly if one of his audience tried to dodge the business of the day, by glancing at a book or newspaper or whispering to his neighbour. He demanded full attention and absolute silence, and that not only within the classroom walls. Hearing a noise in the corridor, he would break off his lecture and return to the subject under discussion only when absolute silence had been established. Apart from such rare, involuntary interruptions, A. Ya. Khinchin was very willing to find room in his lectures for remarks of a purely pedagogical character. Seeing in his listeners future teachers, he would often share with them his ideas on how to treat some mathematical question in order that it should appear as clear, obvious and expressive as possible.

As a teacher in the higher schools, one of A. Ya. Khinchin's most characteristic features was his willingness to tackle very difficult teaching problems, to work out methods for solving them, and, after he was convinced of their effectiveness, to develop and perfect these methods under new conditions. An excellent example of his successes in this direction is provided by his book "Eight lectures on mathematical analysis", which has sustained four Russian editions and has been translated into many other languages. Alexander Yakovlevich decided here to come to the aid of that wide circle of specialists who, having more or less thoroughly mastered the algorithmic side of mathematical analysis—having learnt how to differentiate and integrate—wish to give their knowledge its essential logical and conceptual basis. As A. Ya. Khinchin pointed out, this category of specialists includes not only engineers and economists, but also many teachers and university mathematics students. It is all a matter of setting aside the particular cases and seeing the subject as a whole.

A. Ya. Khinchin began, as he says in the preface to the first edition of the "Eight lectures", with a course of twelve lectures aimed at engineers taking courses to improve their qualifications at Moscow University, and this course, despite its brevity, satisfied the listeners' requests. "I was able to find the right solution to the teaching problem that confronted me"—wrote A. Ya. Khinchin—"and from the very beginning I rejected the thought of setting out even one chapter of my subject in full detail; instead I limited myself to as clear, concise, and expressive a development of principal ideas as was possible. I spoke more of aims and tendencies, of problems and methods of solution, of the inter-relations of the basic concepts of analysis among themselves and with their applications, than of particular theorems and proofs. I was not afraid, in a large number of cases, to refer my students to the text-books to look up the details of proofs (and sometimes even whole chains of theorems and proofs) if they did not have major significance."

Is it not true that here, in a few details, lies one version of the "royal road" to mathematics in our time? But this image of the lecturer's function is important not only for mathematics: it can be confidently recommended—mutatis mutandis —for many lecture courses both in the humanities and the natural sciences: in fact it is in just this direction that we should seek the means of freeing the student's time for independent work.

The concrete realization of Khinchin's ideas is contained in the "Eight Lectures". We need not insist that all the material of the book was covered in a course of precisely eight two-hour lectures. It is a matter of eight chapters, whose sizes vary from 24 to 42 pages of rather small print (we refer to the third edition). Each chapter is devoted to one of the fundamental questions of mathematical analysis. Here are the titles of these chapter-"lectures": I. The continuum. II. Limits. III. Functions. IV. Series. V. The derivative. VI. The integral. VII. The expansion of functions in series. VIII. Differential equations.

In our note we can do no more than mention a few examples of those approaches by the use of which Alexander Yakovlevich was able, from his very first words, to persuade the reader to embark on a programme of serious mental work, and at the same time to feel himself on an equal conversational footing with the author-lecturer. For example, Lecture I, devoted to the study of real numbers, opens with the question, "Why should mathematical analysis start with the study of the continuum?"

The author, after citing the usual definition of a function, emphasizes that in this definition: "as in an embryo, is embodied the whole idea of mastering the phenomena of nature and the processes of technology with the help of mathematical apparatus." This leads us to demand of the definition complete and unimpeachable clarity, and, in particular, a full picture of the set of *all* values that the quantity x can assume. "And in exactly the same way that we must thoroughly study the ground before setting it to bear fruit, so in higher mathematics, if we wish to be farsighted and scientific farmers, rather than those who sow at hazard, we must first study carefully the environment where the concept of functional dependence lives and grows before we construct on its basis the whole edifice of our science". In this way is motivated the importance and necessity of studying the continuum. Further on, the author tells us how all known theories of the continuum "have as their aim to obtain by a single constructive principle, starting from the set of rational numbers as initial data, the whole collection of all real numbers". This allows him to put on firm ground the idea of passage to the limit. It then becomes clear that there is no need to consider all the different methods of building up the theory of real numbers, and that it will be sufficient to consider one of these (the Dedekind theory) as a typical example.

As a second example, let us take the beginning of the third lecture, which is devoted to the concept of a function. Here Alexander Yakovlevich tells his audience that the concept of function introduced in the first lecture was born and rose to victory in a long struggle with the forces of the analytical apparatus, a concept that has greatly impeded the evolution of the idea of functional dependence from the eighteenth century onwards. In order to reveal to the reader the nature of this question, the author invents an imaginary discussion between the "mathematician" and the "engineer" on the question of whether or not a certain set of rules defines a function (the Dirichlet function is considered in particular).

E

The discussion ends, of course, with the complete victory of the mathematician.

In the lecture on the derivative (lecture V) the author convinces the reader that "if we wish to obtain some idea of how quickly the quantity y changes as a result of changes in the independent variable x, how 'sensitive' it is to changes in x, then, of course, we shall somehow or other have to make a comparison, set the two quantities one against the other, compare between themselves the increment in the function y and the increment h in x that has caused the increment in y." As a result, of course, the ratio $\dfrac{f(x+h) - f(x)}{h}$ makes its appearances, and then its limit as h tends to zero.

We shall limit ourselves to these few examples, referring the reader who has never read the "Eight Lectures", or who has read them and already had time to forget them, to the original source, which we have been concerned with here in the first place as an example of the author's teaching mastery.

If, in the "Eight Lectures", Alexander Yakovlevich has brilliantly solved the problem of surveying the essential ideas of a course in mathematical analysis whose main details are already known to the reader, in his "Short course of mathematical analysis" he solves the problem of providing a text-book of analysis that will be limited in its material to the bounds of the compulsory syllabus for the first and second year university students and at the same time constructed on a completely modern scientific level.

In this course, as in the "Eight Lectures", the author does not spare words to ensure that at any given moment the reader is clear as to the appropriateness of the particular route he is following, and that "in introducing new concepts and constructing new theories the pupils should be prepared as soon as possible for the reception of the new material as something natural and even inevitable". A. Ya. Khinchin's views here are well-known to us; the author emphasizes that "only in this way is it possible to implant a real interest in the subject, and not just a formal mastery of its contents". But in contrast to the "Eight Lectures", in the "Short Course" there is no possibility of leaving out details of proofs, or perhaps of whole theorems, that are mentioned in the syllabus. On the contrary, to ease the reader's task, who after all is supposed to be making his first acquaintance with the subject, "all the arguments in the course are carried through down to the minutest details".

Of particular interest in A. Ya. Khinchin's book is his treatment of the theory of limits. The author considers that it is essential to build a bridge between the somewhat vague and intuitive notion of limit that the student brings with him from secondary school and the formal definition using ε and δ, based on the theory of real numbers. To this end he first sets out (in chapter 2) the theory of limits based on the idea of a "process" and its stages, without defining this concept, Later, in chapter 3, the idea of a process is described in mathematical terms, and the concept of limit is correspondingly refined. Finally the necessity of constructing a theory of real numbers is motivated along the lines already familiar to us from the "Eight Lectures" (in this case the Weierstrass theory is used), and thus the theory of limits is completed. In this approach, one can feel the author's exceptional attentiveness towards the reader making his first acquaintance with analysis. Let us remark, however, that the rather narrow concept of a "process" turns out to be insufficient for the later requirements of forming integral sums. Thus for the definition of an integral, the author again has to return to the concept of limit, in order to define the meaning of the limit of an integral sum.

We shall not pause here over the other special features of the "Short Course". We shall remark only that, as well as the examples and problems worked through in detail in the text, Khinchin refers in the appropriate places to small numbers of exercises from the "Collection of exercises and problems in mathematical analysis" by B. P. Demidovich, which are to be worked through in order to better clarify the theory. It is emphasized that further exercises, as indicated by the teacher, would be needed in order to acquire the necessary techniques. The author places no small value on the references to these exercises; at least, in the second edition, a special index is added where the number of the exercise is given according to the new edition of the problem book.

The book closes with a brief but informative historical essay on analysis up to the present day.

If we take into account that the author, in the space of 39 printed pages,[1] sets out the whole two-year course in a style that is fresh, lively, interesting, and readily comprehensible, then Khinchin's great mastery of teaching will be seen in a particularly clear light. There can be no doubt that Khinchin's books on mathematical analysis will be of benefit to many and many a future mathematics student, and will long remain outstanding examples of the ability to speak of a complicated subject in a manner that is always to the point, easy to understand and attractive."

> Academician of the Academy of Pedagogical Sciences
> of the RSFSR, A.I. Markushevich.

[1] i.e. 39 x 16 pages of printed text.

List of Books and Monographs by A. Ya. Khinchin,
with available English Translations

34[1] Fermat's Great Theorem. Gosizdat (1927). GTTI (1932).

35 Fundamental Laws of Probability Theory. Phys. Mat. Fak. M.G.U. (1927); GTTI (1932).

65 Asymptotische Gesetze der Wahrscheinlichkeitsrechnung. Berlin (Springer) (1933); ONTI, 1936. German edition issued in New York (1948; Chelsea).

72 Chance and How Science Treats It. ONTI (1934).

73 Continued Fractions. ONTI (1935) GTTI (1949) Fizmatgiz (1961). English translation, Groningen (1963; P. Noordhoff) by P. Wynn.

92 Limit Laws for Sums of Independent Random Variables. GONTI (1938).

104 Fundamental Mathematical Concepts and Definitions in the Secondary Schools. Uchpedgiz (1941).

113 Mathematical Foundations of Statistical Mechanics. Gostekhizdat (1943). English translation, New York (1949; Dover) by G. Gamow.

116 Eight Lectures on Mathematical Analysis. Gostekhizdat (1945, 1946, 1948). English translation, Boston (1965; D. C. Heath) by I. Zygmund.

118 Elementary Introduction to Probability Theory (with B. V. Gnedenko). Gostekhizdat (1946, 1950, 1952, 1957, 1961). English translation, San Francisco (1961; W. H. Freeman) by W. R. Stahl.

120 Three Pearls of Number Theory, Gostekhizdat (1947, 1949). English translation, Rochester (N.Y.) (1952; Graylock Press) by F. Bagemihl, H. Komm and W. Seidel.

132 On the Analytical Apparatus of Statistical Physics. Trudi Mat. Inst. Akad. Sci. USSR 33 (1950). English translation, Delhi (1963; Hindustan Pub.).

136 Mathematical Foundations of Quantum Statistics. Gostekhizdat (1951).

143 The Entropy Concept in Probability Theory. Usp. Mat. Nauk. 8. (1953), pp. 3–20.

144 A Short Course of Mathematical Analysis. Gostekhizdat (1953). English translarion, Delhi (1960; Hindustan Pub.).

146 Mathematical Methods in the Theory of Mass Service, Trans. Mat. Inst. Akad. Sci. USSR. 49. English translation London (1960; (Griffin) by D. M. Andrews and M. A. Quenouille.

150 On the Fundamental Theorems of Information Theory. Usp. Mat Nauk. 11 (1956) pp. 17–75. (143) and (150) together translated into English under the title "Mathematical Foundations of Information Theory", New York (1957; Dover) by R. A. Silverman and M. D. Friedman.

[1]The numbers refer to the bibliography in the Russian edition of 'Pedagogical Essays'; this has one or two slight differences with the bibliography in Gnedenko's Berkeley address.

List of A. Ya. Khinchin's Publications on Philosophy, Teaching and the History of Mathematics

30   The Ideas of Intuitionism and the Struggle for the Subject in Contemporary Mathematics. Vestnik Komm. Akad. **16**. (1926) pp. 184–92.

38   The Strong Law of Large Numbers and its Significance for Mathematical Statistics. Vestnik Statistiki **29**, (1928) pp. 123–8.

42   The Theory of Numbers: A Summary of its Growth from 1917–27. Mat. Sb. **35**, (1928) supplementary vol. pp. 1–4.

43   On the Role and Character of Induction in Mathematics. Vestnik. Komm. Akad. **1**, (1928) pp. 5–7.

50   Von Mises' Teaching on Probability and the Principles of Physical Statistics. Uspekhi. Fiz. Nauk **9** ,(1929) pp. 141–66.

70   Probability Theory in Pre-revolutionary Russia and in the Soviet Union. Front Nauki i Tekhniki. **7**, (1934) pp. 36–46.

80   Metric Problems in the Theory of Irrational Numbers. Uspekhi Mat. Nauk. No. 1 (1936) pp. 7–32.

97   Introduction of Irrational Numbers; material for the use of teachers. Narkompros RSFSR (1938) pp. 9–12 (reprinted in Mat. v Shkole, No. 3, 1939 pp. 32–4.

98   Complex Numbers (with P. I. Dorf); material for the use of teachers. Narkompros RSFSR (1939) pp. 39-47

101   On the Teaching of Mathematics. Molodaya Gvardia No. 9 (1940) pp. 142–50; reprinted under the title 'Many-sided Practical Education of Soviet Youth.' (103 below).

102   Basic Mathematical Concepts in the Secondary Schools. Mat. v Shkole, No. 4 (1939) pp. 4–22, No. 5 pp. 3–10.

103   Many-sided Practical Education of Soviet Youth. Mat. v Shkole No. 6 (1939), pp. 1–7.

106   On Mathematical Definitions in Secondary Schools. Mat. v Shkole No. 1 (1941), pp. 1–10.

107   On the Concept of the Ratio of Two Numbers. Mat. v Shkole, No. 2 (1941), pp. 13–15.

119   On Formalism in School Mathematics Teaching. Izv. Akad. Pedag. Nauk RSFSR No. 4 (1946), pp. 7–20.

131   The Simplest Linear Continuum. Uspekhi Mat. Nauk. *IV* No. 2 (1949), pp. 180–97.

140   Elements of Number Theory. Encyclopaedia of Elementary Mathematics (1952) Vol. 1, pp. 255–353.

141   The Method of Arbitrary Functions and the Fight Against Idealism in Probability Theory. In the collection 'Philosophical Questions of Contemporary Physics' Izd. Akad. Nauk. (1952), pp. 522–38 (French translation in 'Questions Scientifiques V'. Paris, Editions de la Nouvelle Critique, Vol. 1 (1954), pp. 7–24).

142   The Soviet School of Probability Theory. Chinese Math. J, I (1952), pp. 1–7.

151   On the First Acquaintance With Probability Theory, (with A. M. Yaglom) in Childrens' Encyclopaedia, ed. Akad. Ped. Nauk RSFSR, pp. 211–20.

152 Mises' Frequency Theory and Contemporary Ideas of Probability Theory. Voprosi Filosofii No. 1 (1961), pp. 92–102. No. 2 pp. 77–89.

153 On the Educative Effect of Mathematics Lessons. Mat. Prosveshchenie, Vol. 6 (1961), pp. 7–28 reprinted in Mat. v Shkole No. 3 (1962), pp. 30–44.

154 On so-called 'Problems to be Done in the Head' in the Arithmetic Course. Mat. Prosveshchenie Vol. 6 (1:62), pp. 29–36.

APPENDIX 2

MATHEMATICS TEACHING AND THE SOVIET SCHOOL

Khinchin's articles were written at various periods over the last thirty years, and although many of his comments have a general significance, in other places he was concerned with the defects of a specific education system at a specific point in time. In order to try and put such comments into perspective, and also to explain some of the special vocabulary that is used in describing Soviet education but may be unfamiliar to the general reader, we have thought it worthwhile to include as a final appendix a brief account of the history of Soviet education, a summary of the main features of Soviet schools, and some details of their mathematics courses. At the same time we have taken the opportunity of mentioning some of the more recent developments of Soviet mathematics teaching which, although they take us rather outside the scope of the rest of the book, in several cases are closely linked with ideas developed by Khinchin in his essays many years earlier.

Of course such a brief account must necessarily remain at a rather superficial level and we must refer the reader to other sources to supplement and perhaps even to correct the impressions that follow. In particular, we should mention the historical section in the book edited by G. Z. F. Bereday, the books of A. C. Korol, N. de Witt, and Nigel Grant, the book of essays edited by E. J. King[1], as well as Soviet sources such as M. Deineko[2]. Further references will be cited as we proceed.

We should also like to mention again our indebtedness to Professor B. V. Gnedenko for making available the sample examination questions quoted below, and for permission to reproduce from his recent lectures in Australia and New Zealand the syllabus material contained in Tables 1–4. Although we have benefited greatly from conversations with Professor Gnedenko, the opinions expressed in this appendix, and the responsibility for any errors it may contain, are entirely our own.

Before the revolution, the Russian school system was similar to the school system in other parts of continental Europe, and consisted of

[1]These books are listed in the references at the end of the appendix.
[2] 'Forty years of National Education in the U.S.S.R.' (in Russian) Moscow, 1957.

117

three main components: the elementary schools, the gymnasia (fee-paying schools where the children could continue with a secondary education of classical type), and the real-schools (where more emphasis was given to science and technical subjects). In the field of education, the last fifty years of Tsarist rule could be crudely summarized as a series of concessions to the cause of educational reform, followed by periods of reaction. Their fear of opposition from the schools and universities led the Tsars to institute a closely controlled, bureaucratic educational administration, against which the universities and other advocates of educational reform struggled with varying success in different periods. A law calling for universal elementary education was passed in 1908 but was not due to take full effect until 1922. Although by 1918 further extensive reforms were under way, and the number of pupils in the schools and institutes of higher education was rapidly increasing, it is unlikely even then that more than 50 per cent of the population was literate,[1] and there were still great barriers in the way of children from poor homes who wished to receive higher or even secondary education.

The revolution ushered in a decade of enthusiasm, experiment and confusion. The old school-system was overthrown, and new types of schools were set up based on the 'unified labour school', where teaching and work, or at least work-training, were to be combined. The new government was committed to the use of the schools as a platform for inculcating the ideals and attitudes relevant to the new society, and aimed at abolishing illiteracy and achieving free, universal, compulsory education in the shortest possible time. There was immense enthusiasm for education. University professors were called upon to read lectures in factories and at public meetings; schoolchildren returned home to teach their parents how to read and write. But the country was still ravaged by civil war, wars of foreign intervention, famine, and the immense burdens of its own poverty, backwardness and isolation. It is perhaps something of a tragedy that many interesting experimental ideas were introduced just at this time. Not only were they denied their proper fruit in the sequel, but to some extent they had the effect of hindering the progress of education rather than of helping it; the major problems were to overcome illiteracy and provide basic education for the millions of children throughout the Union, and in the first place these required strong administration and simple principles.

It was only as Stalin tightened his grip on the Soviet scene that an administration emerged strong enough and determined enough to overcome such difficulties. Under his direction, Soviet education was

[1]The 1960 Statistical Handbook 'Narodnoe Khozyaistvo' quotes the following literacy rates: 26 per cent in 1897; 57 per cent in 1926; 91 per cent in 1939. The figures refer only to the population within the age range 9–49.'

rebuilt along lines that are somewhat reminiscent of the pre-revolution-ary model. Formal examinations were re-introduced, together with class-gradings, diplomas, and a fixed school syllabus. The main achieve-ment of this period, roughly the decade 1930–40, was the final realization of universal education. By the end of the nineteen-thirties, the bulk of Soviet children were at school, the main problems of illiteracy had been overcome, primary education at least was compulsory and effectively universal, and the number of universities and institutes of higher education was rapidly multiplying. These were considerable achievements for any government, bearing in mind that only twenty years earlier fifty per cent of the population was illiterate and that much of the first ten years had been spent in bringing order to the country.

The further growth of Soviet education was harshly interrupted by the Second World War. Many millions of children were evacuated, sometimes taking school and teacher with them, sometimes relying on local facilities in their new environment. Thousands of school buildings were destroyed, and many of the generation that should have provided the teachers of these years were called to the front, and either killed or at best lost to the schools. The school programme was interrupted for the purposes of military training, and in 1944 the secondary schools (previously co-educational) were temporarily divided into separate boys' schools and girls' schools. The after-effects of the war continued to be felt for many years, and indeed are still evident today. For several years, teachers in Soviet schools were almost all women, and this imbalance is still not fully righted.[1] The shortage of teachers, already acute because of the rapid expansion of education, became still more difficult. Shortage of school buildings was another problem rendered still more acute. School buildings were often old and cramped, and many schools (even full-time schools) were obliged to work in shifts so as to make maximum use of the limited space available. It appears to be only in the last five years or so that educational buildings have been given urgent priority, and this problem has been somewhat relieved.

Despite these difficulties, education continued to expand. One of the effects of moving many institutes (including Moscow University) to the Central Asian republics during the war was to boost the development of these republics, in education as in many other fields. A particularly important event of the war years was the founding in 1943 of the Academy of Pedagogical Sciences of the RSFSR. Since the Academy

[1]In 'Zhenshchina v SSSR' (1960) the overall percentage of women teachers in the Soviet Union was quoted as 60 per cent in 1940/41; 70 per cent in 1950/51; and 70 per cent in 1958/59. The proportion in the RSFSR alone is higher, 77 per cent in 1958/59.

continues to play a leading role in the formulation of educational policy in the Soviet Union, and Khinchin himself was a full member and a member of its presidium, it may be worthwhile digressing here to discuss briefly the activities of the Academy and its place in the administration of Soviet education. After the revolution, the republics of the Soviet Union instituted People's Commissariats of Education (Narkompros) to take the place of the Tsarist ministries. Until the last few years, there has never been an administrative body for school education at the all-union level (as distinct from the situation for higher education). Major changes in school educational policy came from the Central Committee of the Communist Party, after formal ratification by the Supreme Soviet. The Academy of Pedagogical Science was first attached to the RSFSR Narkompros, later, when in 1946 this changed its name, to the RSFSR Ministry of Education. But since the main branch of the Academy is located in Moscow, and the changes in educational policy introduced into the RSFSR schools are usually faithfully imitated by the other republics, in effect the Academy is an advisory body on educational policy for the whole Union. Its main functions are to carry out research into educational problems in the USSR, to suggest curricula reform and text-book improvements, to advise the Central Committee and the Ministry of Education on questions of educational policy, to publish text-books and other material relevant to its work. The Academy does not appear to be merely a stooge for political interests, and indeed would seem to be a useful counterweight to excesses of political enthusiasm in educational matters. Its members, including the presidium members, number many university professors, who, as Khinchin himself, have won world reputations in their own fields. The Academy also offers a route for airing the grievances and suggestions of practising teachers, since it organizes many lectures and discussions, as well as publishing a number of journals (Sov'etskaya Pedagogika, Voprosy Psikhologii, and Sem'ya i Shkola). In theory, such grievances are handled through what Bereday describes as a 'shuttle service' between the teachers and the Ministry: suggestions for reform are sent to the schools from the Ministry, discussed by the teachers, sent back with comments and further suggestions, etc. In practice, Soviet teachers seem to be very closely held down to a fixed syllabus, and, except in specially selected experimental schools, there is little opportunity for individual teachers to experiment with new choice of material or even new methods of approach.

In its general outline, the system that had been built up during the nineteen-thirties survived both the Second World War and the death of Stalin, and persisted up to the late nineteen-fifties. During this period the main structure of the school programme was not altered. In 1939 it consisted of four years of compulsory primary education (from 8–11) followed by three years of secondary education and three years of upper secondary education. In 1944 the compulsory enrolment age was reduced to 7, but the length of the course remained unaltered. Compulsory secondary education (covering the three years 11–13 or 12–14) was introduced, at first in the towns but spreading later to the country areas as well. It is now claimed to be universal, which is probably true, except perhaps in remote areas. The fifth 5-year plan envisaged compulsory 10-year education in the towns by 1955 and in country districts five years later. However, these plans were never carried through, and towards the end of the 1950's the uniform and somewhat academic courses of the Soviet schools came in for growing criticism. Khrushchev swung the party into a move for 'closer links with real life' in the field of education. In common with most countries of the West, the provision of large numbers of people with specialized technical education suddenly became an urgent national problem. The universities complained that the school courses were old-fashioned, and had failed to take into account modern developments in science and technology.

The upshot of these criticisms was a series of extensive reforms that were mooted in 1956, worked out in detail during 1958, released for public discussion by the Central Committee of the Communist Party in November of that year, and, after some modifications, passed into law one month later. The reforms centred round the rehabilitation of an old principle of communist education (dating back to Marx himself) that the schools should provide not only a general education but also an appreciation of the nature of work in industry and agriculture. The application of this principle (the polytechnic principle, as it is usually called) had been one of the experiments of the period following the revolution that were later put on one side, although the idea had never been entirely discarded. In those days it was linked with the problems of overcoming illiteracy and providing a basic work force for the expanding Soviet industry, and found some expression in terms of the unified labour schools, 'rabfaks' (university or adult education faculties for workers), schools attached to factories, and, later, part-time schools for rural and working youth. In the 1950's, with a widespread system of education already in operation and the problems of technical education already urgent, it could be given a different interpretation. Khrushchev took it to mean that the task of providing the technical training needed for work in modern industry should be borne largely by the schools, and that the structure of the Soviet school system should be altered accordingly. Not only should the child be educated in the usual sense; on leaving school, he should be capable of performing some useful productive task in the community, even if at a later stage he would continue with higher education.

The main provisions of these reforms, on which the present system is based, were as follows. In the first place, the plans for introducing universal ten-year education were dropped, but the period of compulsory education was increased from seven to eight years. In the new eight-year schools, the polytechnic principle made its appearance in the form of workshop training (classes in woodwork, metalwork etc.) and in the last few years, a few weeks' work experience in a factory or on a collective farm. After finishing the eight-year schools, that is to say at the age of about 15 years, the pupil was to have a choice of paths. On the one hand, he could leave the full-time schools and embark on some form of employment. This would not mean that he had completely finished with school education; in the majority of cases he would receive a further period of training, of anything from six months to two or even three years, in a vocational school, or he would continue his education by attending a part-time or correspondence school. The vocational schools took over the trade schools, and to some extent supply the Soviet version of an apprenticeship training, although there is no apprenticeship system as such in the USSR. Their graduates may become mechanics, carpenters, electricians, locomotive drivers—there are even special schools for barbers. The number of formal lessons presumably depends a great deal on the particular trade or skill being taught. The part-time schools include what used to be called the schools for working and rural youth, and their courses may follow the syllabuses of the general schools or of the semi-professional schools described below. In many cases they work in two or sometimes even three shifts a day.

On the other hand, the pupil could continue with a full-time education, either in the schools of general education or in the semi-professional schools. The schools of general education, or more simply the general schools, provide relatively academic courses, and are now usually regarded as the training ground for the institutes of higher education (the universities, engineering institutes, agricultural colleges, pedagogical institutes, medical schools, and so on). In such a school, the pupil would continue his education for a further three years (classes 9, 10 and 11). Although the total period of secondary education was thus increased from six to seven years, there was no essential increase in teaching time, because a further provision of the reforms was that one-third of the time in these last three years was to be spent in 'production training', as part of the polytechnic programme. Exactly what this production training involves in practice is rather hard to pin down, and seems to vary a good deal from place to place and from school to school, depending on the facilities available in the town, shortages in different industries and other factors. On the whole, it appears that in the towns most of the children spend the time for production training actually inside a factory, working beside adults, learning some parti-cular job in the factory or perhaps studying several different aspects of its work. In the country the pupils may receive training in the collective farms and even help in such jobs as bring in the harvest. The production training may also involve lectures and other forms of class-room work. Production training apart, the general schools still follow a uniform syllabus (with slight variations where the native language is not Russian) laid down by the education ministries after recommendations from the Central Committee and consultations with the Academy of Pedagogical Sciences.

The other full-time alternative is made up by the semi-professional schools, such as the technicums. These schools provide courses of from three to four years in length, sometimes with shorter courses (usually two years) for students who have already completed 10 or 11 years in the general schools. As well as rounding off the pupils' general education, they aim at giving them a specialized technical training. The graduates from such schools may become technicians, laboratory workers, engineers, nurses, dentists, primary school teachers —the different courses in different schools cover a very wide range. Most of the schools concentrate on a small group of related subjects. In all, nearly four hundred different options were listed by de Witt (1961). In these schools also, the school courses usually alternate with periods of work or practical training in the chosen subject. In common with the graduates of the general schools, graduates of the semi-professional schools have the right to apply for entrance to the higher educational institutes.

The final main provision of the 1958 reforms was the requirement that before going on to the universities or other institutes of higher education, the student must spend a two-year period of 'productive work' in industry or agriculture. One of the reasons behind this require-ment seems to have been Khrushchev's fear that university graduates were losing contact with the working man and starting to form a bourgeois elite of their own. It also provided an immediate useful increase in the work force. However, in practice this requirement was never fully enforced, and often was completely waived for the students of priority subjects such as mathematics and some of the sciences. Thus an indirect effect of this requirement has been to further raise the prestige of mathematics in Soviet schools and to discriminate against disciplines such as history and literature.

The four main types of school described above—the general schools, the semi-professional schools, the vocational schools and the part-time schools—form the basis of the present Soviet school system. The divisions between the last three types are probably not as clear-cut as we have made them out, but some simplification is necessary to make sense of a very complicated scene. There are in addition some further types of specialized schools, such as the military schools and schools specializing in the fine arts, theatre, music, which take in the children at a rather earlier age—often about 11—and provide an education centred around the special discipline. Here special courses and training take the place of the usual production training. A few special schools provide intensive training in a chosen foreign language. Some publicity has been given to the establishment of boarding schools within the framework of Soviet education, but at present, although their role is certainly increasing, it appears as if the greater part of these schools cater for retarded or difficult children, or for children whose parents for various reasons are unable or unwilling to keep their children at home. With the exception of some of these boarding schools, Soviet school education is free.

It appears to be rather difficult to obtain reliable figures for the proportions of schoolchildren passing on to different types of schools. In any one year, there must be of the order of four to five million students graduating from the eight-year schools. Of these, it would seem that at least two-thirds and possibly as many as ninety per cent continue with some form of further education. Figures published by P. Urban (1961) suggest that about 30 per cent of these are full-time in the general schools, about 20 per cent in the semi-professional schools, 30 per cent in the vocational schools and 20 per cent in part-time general schools.[1] Somewhat similar figures are suggested by J. J. Figueroa (1963),[2] if we assume that his 'part-time' schools include our 'vocational schools'.

Although to venture any further would take us rather beyond the scope of this essay, we should perhaps mention that some of the changes introduced in 1958 seem likely to be rather short-lived. The universities were always opposed to the idea of production training, as, apparently, were several members of the Academy of Pedagogical Sciences.[3] Perhaps as a result of their influence, the time allotted to production training in the general schools has been cut down, and the period of full secondary education reduced from eleven years back to ten years. This has been achieved by cutting back the final three years to two, not by altering the courses of the eight-year schools. These changes are

[1] 'The reorganization of Soviet Education'. East European Surveys II (1962) pp. 89–103. For 1961–62 he reports 4·26 million in the upper classes of the general schools, 3·26 in the part-time schools, 1·26 in vocational schools and 2·37 in specialized (semi-professional) schools. These figures have to be adjusted to take into account the different lengths of courses in the different types of schools.
[2] 'Selection and differentiation in Soviet schools' in E. J. King (ed.) 'Communist Education'. London (Methuen) 1962.
[3] 'The Changing Soviet School' p. 375.

described in more detail in an article by Nigel Grant (1965).[1] On the other hand, the 1958 reforms resulted in at least one movement that is likely to have a profound effect on the future of Soviet education—the introduction of specialized upper secondary schools. We shall say something more about these schools after we have discussed the place of mathematics in the general school syllabus.

* * *

In all Soviet schools, mathematics is a major and compulsory part of the programme. In the eight-year schools, and the final three years of the general schools, a uniform syllabus is laid down for the whole of the USSR. It seems likely that the mathematics courses in the semi-professional and part-time schools are of the same general character, although the emphasis given to mathematics will naturally vary according to the chosen special field. The mathematics courses in the vocational schools are abbreviated, but it seems that even here they cannot be avoided. These remarks are important when it is borne in mind how many Soviet schoolchildren continue their education beyond the first eight-year period. Probably about two-thirds of the children in the Soviet Union would continue their training in mathematics for at least one year beyond this level, at which stage, making a crude comparison from the syllabus content, they might be somewhere near the O-level school certificate standard. About half of the students would continue for another three years or longer beyond the eight-year schools, by which time they would seem to reach a standard (see the examination questions quoted below) somewhere between O-level and A-level. How much is achieved in practice is, of course, very hard to assess—in the part-time schools, for example, it seems certain that the achievements often fall far short of the aims—but the aims alone give some indication of the importance of mathematics in the technically and scientifically oriented programme of Soviet education.

Let us turn now to a more detailed examination of the mathematics courses in the general schools. A break-down of the general school programme into hours/week in different subjects is shown in Table 1 for the eight-year schools, and in Table 2 for the final three years of the general schools. These are for schools of the RSFSR where Russian is the basic language. The breakdown for schools in the other republics would be very similar, save that time would be provided for study both in Russian and the local language.

In the primary schools (ages 7–10), mathematics takes up some 6 hours per week, as compared with 12 hours per week for Russian

---

[1] 'Recent changes in Soviet secondary schools'. Internat. Review of Education XI (2) 1965, pp. 129–143.

TABLE 1

CURRICULUM IN 8-YEAR SCHOOLS

Subject	Class								Total number of instruction hours
	1	2	3	4	5	6	7	8	
1. Russian language	12	12	12	10	6	5	3	2	2184
2. Literature	–	–	–	–	2	3	2	3	357
3. Mathematics	6	6	6	6	6	6	6	5	1663
4. History	–	–	–	2	2	2	2	3	391
5. Nature studies	–	–	–	3	–	–	–	–	105
6. Geography	–	–	–	–	2	2	2	2	286
7. Biology	–	–	–	–	2	2	2	2	286
7. Physics	–	–	–	–	–	2	2	3	249
9. Chemistry	–	–	–	–	–	–	2	2	142
10. Drafting	–	–	–	–	–	–	1	1	71
11. Foreign language	–	–	–	–	4	3	3	3	465
12. Drawing	1	1	1	1	1	1	1	–	248
13. Music and singing	1	1	1	1	1	1	1	1	283
14. Sport	2	2	2	2	2	2	2	2	566
15. Laboratory work	2	2	2	2	3	3	3	3	709
16. Physical labour	–	–	2	2	2	2	2	2	426
17. Two weeks of production experience after 5, 6, 7 and 8 years of instruction									180
							Grand Total		8611

The figures in the body of the table represent the number of hours per week allotted to the given subject.

TABLE 2

CURRICULUM IN GRADES 9–11 OF SOVIET 11-YEAR SCHOOLS

Subject	Class			Total number of hours
	9	10	11	
1. Literature	3	3	3	339
2. Mathematics	4	4	4	452
3. History and elements of political science	3	3	4/6	410
4. Economic geography	–	2	2/0	112
5. Physics	4	4	2	382
6. Astronomy	–	1	–	39
7. Biology	3	–	–	117
8. Chemistry	2	3	2	265
9. Drafting	2	–	–	78
10. Foreign language	2	2	3	261
11. Sport	2	2	2	226
12. Production training	12	12	12	1356
			Grand total	4037

The figures in the body of the table represent the number of hours per week allotted to the given subject.

language, and a total teaching time of 24 hours per week. The lessons are concerned with giving an understanding of initial concepts, numbers, mensuration, and elementary problems in arithmetic. From the very first, their lessons have something of a formal character, with rota learning, answers by the class in unison, and numerous, repetitive exercises as the typical classroom techniques.

For the first four years of secondary school, the total school time increases from 24 to 36 hours per week. Mathematics retains its number of 6 hours per week, but Russian language and literature drops to 8 hours in classes 5 and 6, and to 5 hours in classes 7 to 8. The extra time goes on new subjects. A foreign language (3–4 hours per week), history, geography and biology (2 hours a week each) all make their appearance in class 5; physics (2–3 hours per week) appears in class 6 and chemistry (2 hours per week) in class 7.

Within the mathematics course, fractions and decimals are taken in class 5; proportions, percentages and the first notations of algebra in class 6; linear equations, factorization of simple polynomials, graphs, and simple theorems of geometry in class 7; logarithms, square roots and quadratic equations, trigonometric functions of an acute angle, geometry of circles and similar triangles in class 8.

The child's progress from year to year is assessed on the basis of the term's work, supplemented by oral examinations. The oral examinations proceed in the following manner. Some weeks before the examination, a collection of billets is placed on the notice board, each billet containing three questions, the total aggregate of questions giving a fair coverage of the required syllabus. On the day of the examination, when his turn arrives, the pupil is given one of these billets at random (i.e. without knowing in advance which billet he will get), allowed ten minutes or so to collect his thoughts, and then called in front of the examiners. For an examination in mathematics, the examiners will then ask him to work his questions out on the blackboard, explaining each step as he goes along.

After the eight-year schools, state examinations are held. There are two examinations in mathematics, a three-hour written examination in arithmetic and algebra, and an oral examination in algebra and geometry. A typical billet for the oral examination might be made up as follows:

Question 1   Derive the formula expressing the side of a right polygon in terms of the radius of the escribed circle.

Question 2   Solve numerically a problem concerning the length of the circumference or the area of a circle.

Question 3   Calculate the area of a triangular plot of ground, given a plan of the plot.

The final choice of question within this general framework would be left to the teacher taking the class.

The final three years of the general secondary schools have a rather different character because of the time spent on production training. Very often, this time may be lumped together rather than spread out over the year, but we shall continue to use the average numbers of hours per week as a convenient way of assessing the syllabus.

The formal part of the course forms a direct extension of the work of the first four years of the secondary schools. The total time available for this part of the course is now only 24 hours per week, the remaining 12 hours being spent in production training. Of this 24 hours, mathematics receives 4 hours, Russian language and literature 3 hours, history and political studies 3–4 hours, a foreign language 2–3 hours. Among the science subjects, physics and chemistry now take precedence (from 2 to 4 hours per week each) while biology is dropped after the 9th class.

Within the mathematics course, the programme for the 9th class covers the solution of triangles, trigonometric functions of an arbitrary angle, division of polynomials, and simple rational algebraic functions; the graph of the exponential function, rational and irrational numbers. The course for class 10 includes the addition theorems for trigonometric functions; simple theorems of solid geometry, including surface areas and volumes of simple solid figures; the exponential and logarithmic functions; simple numerical sequences. Finally, in class 11, the student is introduced to the ideas of limit, continuous function, derivative of a function, and complex number.

Under the latest reforms, by which the last three years of secondary schooling were cut back to two years, few important changes were introduced into the actual content of the syllabuses. The table shown in the article by Nigel Grant mentioned earlier indicates that neither the balance of emphasis nor the total number of hours was very greatly affected by these reforms. The shorter overall period is largely compensated for by the reduction of time spent on production training and consequently freed for the conventional courses.

Further information about the mathematics courses in the last three classes can be obtained by a study of the syllabus for the entrance examinations to institutes of higher education. The 1964 syllabus for the entrance examination to specialized (semi-professional) schools, on the basis of a complete 10 or 11 year education in the general schools, is set out below.[1] It coincides with the syllabus published in 1961 by Moscow State University,[2] so that no radical changes in the general school programme seem to have taken place in this period. Since the syllabus does not include any mention of coordinate

[1] This syllabus is taken from the 'Question Book for entrance candidates to institutes of specialized secondary education', Moscow, 1964.
[2] 'Question Book for entrance candidates to Moscow State University', Moscow, 1961.

geometry or the calculus, it seems reasonable to suppose that, although these subjects may be recommended for study in the final year at school, it has not yet been considered possible to include them as part of the basic programme for the whole country.[1]

Some sample questions are shown following the syllabus. These questions are taken from the written examinations set by the mathematics and physics faculties of Moscow State University. In general, examinations in mathematics are prescribed not only for entrance to the faculties of mathematics and physics, but to those of most other science subjects, as well as to the engineering and technical colleges and to the semi-professional schools. The mathematics and physics faculties prescribe both written and oral examinations in mathematics, whereas an oral examination only is required for other subjects such as chemistry and geology. The candidate's performance is assessed on a scale of five marks, and selection of students is based on a weighted total taken over all examinations (the other examinations include Russian language, and a foreign language). In interpreting these questions it should be borne in mind that the universities in the Soviet Union take in only the top ten per cent or so of the students passing on to some form of higher education, and that of all the universities, Moscow sets the highest standards, passing perhaps as few as one out of five or even one out of ten of the entrance candidates. Moreover, the students are not selected from the Moscow region alone, but come from all parts of the Soviet union.

See, however, the note added in proof at the end of this appendix (p. 162).

*Summary of the Syllabus for the Entrance Examination in
Mathematics for Institutes of Higher Education and
Specialized Secondary Education* (1964)

Arithmetic and Algebra

Real and complex numbers; square root, arithmetic and geometric mean of real numbers; algebraic and geometrical forms of complex numbers.

Manipulation of algebraic expressions including rational functions; simple identities involving squares and cubes; factorization and division of polynomials; simplification of expressions involving quadratic roots.

Equations and inequalities; linear and quadratic equations; sets of linear equations and simple types of quadratic equations; binomial equations, solution of problems leading to such equations; manipulation of inequalities.

Functions and their graphs; linear, quadratic functions and the function $1/x$.

Sequences; arithmetic and geometric progressions; the concept of limit.

Logarithms; identity $a^{\log_a b} = b$; graph of logarithmic and exponential functions; solution of exponential and logarithmic equations using 4–figure tables.

Combinations and binomial theorem; formulae for permutations and combinations; the identity $C_m^n = C_{n-m}^n$; general term in binomial expansion; sums of binomial terms.

Geometry (Plane Geometry)

Straight line, triangle, circle; circles inscribed and escribed to a triangle.

Similar triangles and polygons; right polygons; relations between sides of right polygons, interior and exterior angles, inscribed and escribed circles and their radii.

Circumference of a circle; the number π; area and circumference as limits.

Simple loci and constructions; perpendiculars and bisectors; proportional segments in a circle.

Geometry (Solid Geometry)

Straight line, perpendicular and plane; the three perpendiculars; dihedral angles; the angle between a line and a plane.

Prism; parallelopiped; complete and truncated pyramids. Sides, surfaces, and volumes of prisms and pyramids; surface and volume of cylinder, cone, and truncated cone; spheres; intersections of sphere and plane; surface and volume of sphere; tangent planes; great circles; segments, sectors and sections of sphere.

Trigonometry

Definitions and general properties of trigonometric functions; angular and radial measure; numerical values of trigonometric functions for special values; periodicities of trigonometric functions; relations between the trigonometric functions of a single argument; reduction to functions of an acute angle; graphs of the functions.

Transformation of trigonometric expressions and solution of trigonometric equations; addition formulae for sin, cos, tan; formulae for double and half angles; simple trigonometrical equations and their general solution using the notation arcsin x etc.

Solution of triangles; use of logarithmic tables; sine and cosine theorems; applications of trigonometry to geometrical problems.

Selection of Questions from the Written Entrance Examination in Mathematics, Moscow State University

The questions are given in billets of four questions, one billet to each candidate.

Billet 1 (Mathematics faculty, 1961)

Question 1 Four pipes lead into a swimming pool. When the 1st, 2nd and 3rd pipes are opened, the pool fills in 12 minutes; when the 2nd, 3rd and 4th are opened, in 15 minutes, and when only the 1st and 4th are opened, in 20 minutes. How long will the basin take to fill, when all four are opened?

Question 2 Show that for any whole number n, the number $4^n + 15n - 1$ is divisible by 3 and by 9.

Question 3 A point M is given inside an angle. Draw a line through M in such a way as to cut off from the angle a triangle of least possible area. Show the method of construction of the line.

Question 4 In a right triangular truncated pyramid, a sphere is inscribed touching all 5 faces of the pyramid. The length of the edge of the pyramid is equal to the length of the edge of the smaller base. Find the volume of the truncated pyramid.

Billet 2 (Mathematics faculty, 1962)

Question 1 An uneven number of stones lay along a road at a distance of 10 metres one from the next. The stones had to be collected together at the place where the middle stone was lying. A man could carry only one stone at a time, and he therefore transferred them in sequence, starting from one of the end stones. After transferring all stones, the man had covered a total distance of 3 km. How many stones were there?

Question 2 Solve the equation
$$(\log_2 x^4)^{\frac{1}{2}} + 4 \log_4 (2/x)^{\frac{1}{2}} = 2$$

Question 3 The base of a pyramid is a right-angled triangle, and the faces of the pyramid passing through the sides forming the right angle makes angles of 30° and 60° with the base. A right circular cone is described, about the pyramid, having the same vertex as the pyramid. Find the volume of the cone, if the height of the pyramid is equal to h.

Question 4 In how many zeros does the product of all whole numbers from 1 to 1962 terminate?

Billet 3 (Physics faculty, 1962)

Question 1 By eliminating θ and ϕ from the equations
$$p \operatorname{ctg}^2\theta + q \operatorname{ctg}^2\phi = 1$$
$$p \cos^2\theta + q \cos^2\phi = 1$$
$$p \sin\theta = q \sin\phi$$
find the relation between p and q.

Question 2 Solve the inequality
$$(\tfrac{1}{4})^{2\sin x} - 3(\tfrac{1}{4})^{\sin x} < -2 \quad \text{for } 0 < x < 2\pi$$

Question 3 Solve the equation
$$1 + \sin x + \sin 2x + \sin 3x = \cos x + \cos 3x - \cos 2x$$

Question 4 In a triangle ABC the sides a = 2, b = 3, and the angle C = 60°. Find the radii of the circles passing through each pair of vertices and the centre of the circumcircle.

Question 5 In a right rectangular pyramid the angle between the side faces is equal to σ. Find the distance from the vertex of the pyramid to the centre of the inscribed sphere, if the radius of this sphere is equal to R.

In addition to the formal school courses, it is necessary to say a little about the extra-curricular activities that supplement them. Extra-curricular activities play a large role in the life of Soviet schoolchildren. They are closely linked to and often directly organized by the Komsomol or its junior counterpart the Pioneers. School clubs or circles cater for the widest variety of interests, not only in sport and such activities as music, drama, woodwork, but also in different subjects such as biology, geology, and, by no means least, mathematics. Success in these activities is an important corollary to success in class and almost a pre-requisite for obtaining the best reports on leaving school. Bereday et al remark[1] 'It is clear that circle activities are not merely a leisure-time entertainment for school pupils and students. They serve a serious purpose in the scheme of education and character formation in the Soviet Union'. In addition to the work of the school circles during the terms, summer camps are organized, with a programme of lectures and other activities centred on a given subject.

In mathematics perhaps more than in any other subject, the school circles have come to play a quite indispensible part in supplementing the rather barren territory outlined in the official school syllabus, and in developing and picking out mathematical talent among the schoolchildren. The school mathematical circles are usually organized by the students, post-graduate students and junior staff members of the mathematics faculty of the nearest university or other institute of higher education. They meet once a week, often on Saturdays, and follow up whatever programmes seem best suited to the interests of the pupils in the group or of the people running it. Attendance is voluntary, and is usually made up of the mathematics enthusiasts from the upper forms of a group of neighbouring schools. The activities of the mathematical circles culminate in the yearly 'mathematical olympiads'. The first experiments in organizing these competitions were already under way several years before the war, and by now they have become an integral part of the whole mathematics teaching programme and are organized on a nation-wide basis. From the local circles, competitors can pass on to town, state, interstate and even international competitions. The final problems, although they require little formal mathematics, may be extremely difficult. Several collections of questions from these competitions have been published recently[2] but for the sake of illustration we include below a complete set from Moscow, on which the reader may like to try his teeth if he has no better occupation. Separate competitions are held for each class, from class 7 onwards.

[1] 'The Changing Soviet School', p. 387.
[2] See bibliography.

QUESTIONS

*Problems set in 24th Mathematical Olympiad organized
by Moscow State University, 1961*

7th Class—1st Round

1. Show that if n is an even number, then the numbers $1, 2, 3 \ldots n^2$ can be made up into an n x n table in such a way that the sum of the elements in every column has the same value.

2. Given any 3-figure number abc, form the number cba and subtract the smaller of these two numbers from the larger. Obtaining in this way the number $a_1 b_1 c_1$, perform a similar operation on it; etc.

Show that at some step we shall reach either the number 0 or the number 495 (by abc is meant the three-figure number written out using the three figures a, b, and c).

3. Given an acute-angled triangle $A_0 B_0 C_0$. Let A_1, B_1, C_1 be the centres of the squares on the sides $B_0 C_0, C_0 A_0, A_0 B_0$ respectively. The triangle $A_2 B_2 C_2$ is then formed in a similar way from the triangle $A_1 B_1 C_1$, etc. Show that the triangle $A_{n+1} B_{n+1} C_{n+1}$ cuts the triangle $A_n B_n C_n$ in exactly six points.

4. 100 points are laid out on a plane in such a way that the distance between any two of them is not greater than 1, and if A B C are any three of the points then the triangle ABC is obtuse angled. Show that it is possible to draw a circle of radius $\frac{1}{2}$ on the plane in such a way that all the given points lie either inside or on the circumference of the circle.

5. Two squares of the same colour are chosen on a chessboard. Show that a rook, starting from the first square, can visit every square exactly once while visiting the second square twice.

7th Class—2nd Round

1. The sides of an arbitrary convex polygon are coloured on the outside. A certain number of diagonals are drawn in, in such a way that no three intersect in a single point. Each of these diagonals is also coloured on one side (i.e. on one side of the line a thin coloured strip is drawn). Show that at least one of the polygons into which these diagonals divide the original polygon is coloured outside all round.

2. In a square ABCD a point P is taken on the side AB, a point Q on the side BC, a point R on the side CD and a point S on the side DA; it happens that the figure PQRS is a rectangle. Show that the rectangle PQRS is then either a square, or has the property that its sides are parallel to the diagonals of the original square.

3. Show that among any 39 consecutive natural numbers there must be at least one for which the sum of the digits is divisible by 11.

4. A 4×4 table is made up, in certain cells of which a star is placed. Show that it is possible to place 7 stars in such a way that if any two rows and any two columns of the table are crossed out, there is at least one star left in the remaining part of the table. Show that if there are fewer than seven stars, then it is always possible to cross out two rows and columns of the table in such a way as to leave the remaining cells empty.

5. Show that there do not exist whole numbers a,b,c,d satisfying the equations
$$abcd - a = 1961$$
$$abcd - b = 961$$
$$abcd - c = 61$$
$$abcd - d = 1.$$

8th Class—1st Round

1. Given a triangle ABC and a point O. M_1, M_2, M_3 are the centres of gravity of the triangles OAB, OBC, OCA respectively. Show that the area of the triangle $M_1 M_2 M_3$ is equal to 1/9 of the area of ABC.

2. Two persons are playing a game: one of them makes a selection of natural numbers $(x_1, x_2 \ldots x_n)$ of the same sign, either positive or nagative. The second is allowed to ask, what is the sum of $a_1x_1 + \ldots + a_nx_n$ where $(a_1 \ldots a_n)$ is any set of numbers. What is the least number of questions which will suffice to determine the chosen selection?

3. See question 3 in the 1st round questions for 7th class.

4. Prove that a rook can visit all squares of a rectangular chessboard, passing through each square exactly once, only if the number of squares on the board is even.

5. Two segments of the sequence of natural numbers, each of 1961 members, are written one below the other. Show that each of them can be so rearranged that when the pairs of numbers in the same column are added together, another sequence of natural numbers is obtained.

8th Class—2nd Round

1. Given a figure made up of 16 line segments as in the diagram

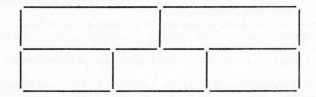

Prove that it is impossible to draw a zigzag line which will cross each of the segments exactly once. The line need not be closed, but its corners must not lie on the segments nor must it pass through any vertices of the figure.

2. With centres at the vertices of a rectangle four circles are constructed with radii r_1, r_2, r_3, r_4 where $r_1 + r_3 = r_2 + r_4 = d$, the diagonal of the rectangle. Two pairs of external tangents are drawn to circles 1, 3 and 2, 4. Prove that a circle can be inscribed in the quadrangle formed by these four lines.

3. See question 3 in the 2nd round questions for 7th class.

4. See question 4 in the 2nd round questions for 7th class.

5. Given a quadruple of numbers a,b,c,d. From these the new quadruple ab, bc, cd, da, is formed by multiplying each number by its successor, and the fourth number by the first. From this quadruple a third quadruple is formed by the same process, etc. Show that in the sequence of quadruples formed in this way no two are equal, save in the case $a = b = c = d = 1$.

9th Class—1st Round

1. See question 1 in the 1st round questions for 8th class.

2. See question 2 in the 1st round questions for 8th class.

3. Show that it is possible to arrange the numbers 1 to n^2 in an n x n table in such a way that the sum of the numbers in each column are equal.

4. In a bus without a conductor (i.e. where the 5 kopeck fare is dropped into a box and a ticket torn off by the passenger himself) 4k passengers are travelling. Each passenger has with him only 10, 15 and 20 kopeck pieces. Show that if the

total number of coins is less than 5k, the passengers cannot pay their fares correctly. Construct an example where it is possible for all passengers to pay the correct fare and the total number of coins is equal to 5k.

5. Given N points in the plane. If ABC are any three of the points, then none of the other points lie within the triangle ABC. Show that the N points can be enumerated in such a way that the polygon $A_1 A_2 \ldots A_N$ is convex.

9th Class—2nd Round

1. The points A and B move with constant and equal angular velocities around the circles O_1 and O_2 respectively (in a clockwise direction). Show that the vertex C of the right-angled triangle ABC also moves with constant angular velocity around a certain circle.

2. In an m x n table certain numbers are inscribed. It is permitted to change simultaneously the signs of all the numbers in one column and of all the numbers in one row. Show that by repeated application of this operation it is possible to transform the given table into one in which the sums of the numbers in any row or column are positive.

3. n points are joined by line segments in such a way that each point is joined to at least one other and there are no two points which can be linked together by two different paths. Show that the total number of line segments is equal to n-1.

4. a, b, p are any numbers. Show that there are mutually prime numbers k, v such that ak + bv is divisible by p.

5. Kolya and Petya are dividing up 2n + 1 nuts, n > 2, and each wishes to obtain as many nuts as possible. Three possible schemes of division are suggested (each takes place in 3 stages).

Stage 1: Petya divides the nuts into two heaps, in each of which there are at least 2 nuts.

Stage 2: Kolya divides each heap into 2 again, in each new part there being at least one nut.

Stages 1 and 2 are the same for all three schemes.

Stage 3: (i) For the first variant Kolya takes the largest and the smallest of the four parts.

 (ii) For the second variant Kolya takes the two middle parts.

 (iii) For the third variant Kolya takes either the smallest and the largest or the two middle parts, but for the right of choosing gives Petya one nut.

 Find out which scheme is the most advantageous for Kolya, and which the least advantageous.

10th Class—1st Round

1. Given a numerical sequence $U_1, U_2, \ldots$; $U_1 = U_2 = 1$ and $U_{n+2} = U_n + U_{n+1}$. Show that U_{5k} is divisible by 5 for k = 1,2, . . .

2. A number of strips of different thicknesses are set out on a plane. No two of them are parallel. How should they be moved parallel to themselves so as to make the area of their common part a maximum?

3. k people travel in a bus without a conductor,* and all of them have only 10, 15, and 20 kopeck pieces. It is known that each was able to pay his 5-kopeck fare, receiving exact change. Show that the smallest number of coins which they could have had among them is $k + \left[\dfrac{k + 3}{4} \right]$, where by [a] is meant the greatest integer not exceeding a.

* See Q.4 for 1st round of class 9.

4. The circle S and the point O lie in a plane, with the point O outside the circle. An arbitrary sphere is drawn through the circle S, and a cone described with vertex O, touching the sphere. Find the locus of the centre of the circle along which the cone touches the sphere.

5. It is known that $Z_1 + Z_2 + Z_3 \ldots + Z_n = O$, where the Z_k are complex numbers. Show that among these numbers there are two whose arguments differ by greater than 120°.

10th Class—2nd Round

1. Show that for any three infinite sequences of natural numbers

$$a_1, \ldots, a_n, \ldots$$
$$b_1, \ldots, b_n, \ldots$$
$$c_1, \ldots, c_n, \ldots$$

there can be found numbers p, q such that $a_p \geqslant a_q$, $b_p \geqslant b_q$ and $c_p \geqslant c_q$.

2. Into a rectangle with sides 20 and 25 units, 120 squares are thrown, each with side 1 unit. Show that inside the rectangle a unit circle may be drawn which does not intersect any of the squares.

3. Certain numbers are inscribed in the squares of an m x n table. In any one operation it is permitted to change the sign of any one row or any one column. Show that by repeating this operation it is possible to change the table into one for which the sums of the entries in any row and any column are non-negative.

4. The distances of a fixed point P of the plane to two vertices A, B of an equilateral triangle ABC are AP = 2, BP = 3. Find the maximum value that can be taken by the length PC as the triangle ABC varies.

5. Given an arbitrary collection of 2^k numbers each equal either to +1 or to −1. A new set is obtained from it by the following rule: each number is multiplied by that following it; the final 2^k-th number is multiplied by the first. From this new set another is formed in a similar way, etc. Show that ultimately a set will be formed consisting solely of units (+1).

From the point of view of the education system as a whole, the work of the school circles and the olympiad competitions has two main practical consequences. In the first place it helps to rouse the children's real interest in mathematics, to supplement the material of the school courses, and to get away from the rather routine, formal exercises of the classroom. This aspect of their work is closely allied to Khinchin's suggestions for overcoming the problem of formalism in the school mathematics programme. It must be counted extremely successful, and the Russian experiments have been copied by many other countries. In addition to the weekly meetings and the olympiads, a number of excellent popular texts have been written expressly with the needs of the school circles in mind. Many of these are also recommended to the mathematics students in the pedagogical institutes. Quite a number of these books have now been translated into English, and we include in the general bibliography at the end of the appendix a list of two series of such translations, the series 'Popular lectures in mathematics', edited by I. N. Sneddon and M. Stark, published by Pergamon, and the other series, 'Topics in Mathematics', included in the 'Survey of Recent East

European Mathematical Literature', edited by A. L. Putnam and I. Wirzup at Chicago University.

The second practical role of the school circles and olympiads is in assisting the universities and other institutes of higher education to select students for their mathematics faculties. Their role here is presumably not a direct one—selection is officially made on the basis of the entrance examination and the children's school records—but an indirect one resulting from the fact that the regular members of the school circles, and the winners in the local olympiad competitions, may be already familiar to the university staff, or at least will have their achievements mentioned in their school records. Such knowledge might enable the universities to retain able students who had done badly in the examinations and might otherwise be rejected. Certainly the universities strongly advise those who intend entering their mathematics faculties to take an active part in the circles and competitions, particularly if they have spent some time in production after leaving school.[1] On the other hand, overmuch reliance on the results of such competitions has been criticized by other mathematicians, who point out that many able mathematicians might be quite incapable of solving olympiad conundrums in the nervous conditions of the competitions, and that such competitions therefore select for only one type of mathematical ability, whereas many other types may be equally valuable in the universities or in research.

A. N. Kolmogorov said in a newspaper article:[2]

'If we seek the means to find *all* children of such an age (14–16) who could successfully choose mathematics as their career, there is no other path save through prolonged, systematic work on raising the standards of mathematics schools, the organization of a network of mathematical circles that would be accessible to students from *every* school, the printing of mass editions of popular books on mathematics, supplementary to the school texts, and the reading of popular lectures on mathematics. And finally, after such long training, the organization of olympiads.'

Despite the rather back-breaking prospect conjured up by these words, it must be admitted that the Soviet school system has moved a considerable distance along the road towards providing his requirements.

*   *   *

Having thus obtained a rough picture of the history and structure of Soviet education, let us now turn to the more difficult but perhaps more

---

[1] This is one of several interesting points raised in A. N. Kolmogorov's little booklet 'A Mathematician's Profession' (3rd edition, Moscow University Press, 1959) which is meant as a guide for schoolchildren about to enter a university and trying to decide their choice of career.

[2] 'The Search for Talent' Izvvestiya, 7th April 1963.

interesting problem of trying to elucidate some of the factors that Soviet mathematicians have seen as weaknesses of school mathematics teaching, and the proposals they have put forward or adopted for remedying them. To attempt a detailed analysis of such questions would be beyond our powers with the scattered material at our disposal, but we shall try to put together a few comments that may help to throw some light on the general scene.

The first article in the Russian edition of Khinchin's pedagogical essays was published in 1939 under the title 'On the teaching of mathematics'[1] and later in the same year under the title 'A many-sided, practical education for Soviet Youth'. We have not translated this article in full in the present collection, since most of the points which have a general application are made at greater length in his other articles, and the remainder is specifically concerned with particular difficulties of Soviet mathematical education at that particular epoch. However, precisely for this reason, the article has some historical interest, and we shall therefore start the discussion by quoting here some extracts.

In his opening paragraph, Khinchin says

'At the present time, mass mathematics teaching is in a state which does not even approach the desirable. In the first instance this must be put down to unsatisfactory syllabuses—at times downright faulty—in all sections of the mathematics programmes taught in both primary and secondary schools.'

Referring to a critical editorial that had appeared sometime earlier in Pravda, he continues,

'If this Pravda article brought up the example of a pupil familiar with the theory of electrons but unable to cope with the elementary hazards of electrical wiring in the apartment, then the situation in mathematics is even worse; the pupil not only has insufficient practical knowledge, but his knowledge does not even cover the major discoveries of the last three centuries. Our syllabuses represent an unsuccessful copy of the prerevolutionary syllabuses, and, with rare exceptions, leave the scientific development of the student at the level of the seventeenth century.'

These considerations lead him to themes that are developed at greater length in his later articles and have also been echoed by many subsequent writers. We can briefly summarize these themes as follows: the need to reform the school mathematics syllabus; the need to develop a creative, active understanding of the subject material and not merely a formal memorization of rules, theorems and definitions; the need to improve the training of mathematics teachers.

Since the second of these themes is given a full treatment in his article on formalism in school mathematics teaching, and later writers

---

[1]See bibliography of Khinchin's works nos. (101), (103).

have added little new to the ideas expressed there, we shall not spend much time on this question here. Among the active steps that have been put forward to implement such ideas, one might include the organization of the olympiad competitions, the printing of popular texts such as those listed in the preceding section, and, following the 1958 reforms, the use of more realistic illustrative material and examples, and of teaching aids (paper and strong models, slide rules, planimeters and other instruments, simple mechanical models).

The other two themes—syllabus reform and teacher training—both raise major questions for any contemporary education system, and in what follows we shall attempt to treat each of them in turn. We must emphasize again that our comments are no more than a few sketchy remarks based on the rather haphazard material that we have been able to collect, and make no claims to be a thorough or authoritative treatment.

Minor details of syllabus reform, such as the improvements suggested by Khinchin in the elementary arithmetic courses, have no doubt been the subject of continual discussion since the syllabus was first put forward, and must have led to many minor changes, changes in emphasis and treatment, changes in the notes attached to the syllabus, and so on. Up to the present time, however, there seem to have been very few major changes in the mathematics courses[1], and we have already commented on the old-fashioned flavour of the school-leaving syllabus and the continued absence of coordinate geometry and introductory calculus from the school programme. Some advances have been made, no doubt as a result of Khinchin's influence as much as anybody's, in introducing the study of the real and complex number systems, simple limits, and the general concept of a function. The 1958 reforms brought certain changes[1] but these were more concerned with improvements in illustrative material and teaching aids, and increasing the emphasis on applications, than with alterations to the basic syllabus.

Of course, the syllabus did not pass through this period free from criticism, and Khinchin's 1939 article, which we shall now quote at greater length, contained a strong section on the need to introduce the elements of the calculus. His references to Engels in this respect may sound a little forced to Western ears; perhaps he felt it was the only way to convince staunch party members in the Narkompros.

> The most categorical need is for the introduction of the elements of the infinitesimal calculus into the school programme. Absolutely everything speaks in favour of this. The infinitesimal calculus is unquestionably one of the greatest achievements of human civilization, comparable to the theory of evolution in biology and the molecular theories in physics and chemistry. If we wish to raise the

[1]See, however, the note added in proof at the end of this appendix.

cultural and scientific level of the worker and kolkhoznik to the level of technician or engineer, how can we look unmoved at the absence from the school mathematics syllabus of the mathematical basis of all contemporary technology? Still more, infinitesimal analysis plays a most important role in forming the scientific, dialectic-materialistic world-view. Engels has frequently referred to the fact that dialectics enter mathematics with the differential and integral calculus, and no one knows better than we mathematicians how very true his words are.

All the oft-repeated objections to the introduction of infinitesimal analysis into the secondary school courses are either based on erroneous suppositions, or refer to difficulties that can be overcome by the schools quite fully and without sacrifice. It is not true that the mastery of this section would present especial difficulties for the pupils; those who, in their time, studied at the real-school will remember that a mastery of the elements of analysis was acquired much more easily than many parts of, say, three-dimensional geometry, to say nothing of solving head-splitting geometrical problems. It is not true that teaching the calculus would present disproportionate difficulties for our teachers: given good text-books and good will, there is not the slightest doubt that both young teachers and the older members of our teaching staffs could cope successfully with the new problems. And finally, it is not true that the 10-year schools could not find room for the fundamentals of elementary analysis in their already overburdened programmes. It is indeed true that these programmes are overburdened, but we must look carefully to see what they are overburdened *with*: among their contents is much that has neither instructional value in forming the pupil's world-view, nor practical application, and is retained only for the sake of blind tradition. What instructional value have all these 'special cases' for the solution of obtuse-angled triangles, of 'inverse', 'trinomial' and other sorts of equations, all the head-splitting three-dimensional problems in geometry, and much more? What comparison can be made between all this and infinitesimal analysis, serving for almost three hundred years as the main fundament for mathematical science and the chief mathematical tool in the natural sciences and technology? Without any regrets and without the slightest hesitation, we should throw out from the school course all archaism, all those things that are retained in these programmes only because that is how our parents and grandparents were taught. If we have driven out the letter 'Yat' from our writing, that is no excuse for allowing it to build itself a nest in school mathematics . . .

Of course, the introduction of infinitesimal analysis into our school programme must not be done simply by copying the old real-school where everything was taught in the style and spirit of elementary mathematics, and the elements of coordinate geometry and differential calculus appeared only in the very last class as a series of mechanical instructions. Of course, we desire and demand more. Our programme must be constructed so that the pupils should master the idea of a changing quantity and of functional dependence—representing the direct mathematical reflection of the basic characteristics of the dialectic world-view—as early as possible; these ideas should become as soon as possible the basic pivot of the whole school mathematics course. The elements of analysis must not be an 'appendix' but must lie at the hub of the syllabus, must form one of its indispensible, organic constituents, and must be tied with the strongest threads to all its basic themes.

It is rather remarkable that Khinchin's arguments have not borne more fruit, especially in the last decade or so. However, up till now the Soviet school authorities seem to have been obliged to set their hand against the introduction of calculus into the school course

F

(possibly from the shortage of qualified teachers) and also against the further innovations (set theory, elements of group theory and much else) that have been such a subject of discussion in the West. Without spending any time on the intervening period, we should like to quote on this theme a recent article[1] by Professor Markushevich, at present one of the leading figures in the field of Soviet mathematical education, which perhaps summarizes the present Soviet view on these questions.

Professor Markushevich starts his article by discussing briefly some of the various reform movements in school mathematics teaching that have appeared during the last half-century or so, starting from Felix Klein's 'Erlangen Programme'. He points out that although the basic ideas of Klein's reforms still deserve serious attention, and indeed have already led to many improvements in school syllabuses throughout the world, the last sixty years have seen such advances in mathematics—in particular the simplifications which can be brought about by the abstract study of elementary mathematical structures, and the increasing role of 'finite mathematics'—that it is perhaps necessary to somewhat reduce the emphasis on infinitesimal analysis that characterized Klein's suggestions. A second group of important developments, such as the increasing uses of mathematical logic, have led to the idea that the actual process of learning in the schoolchild's mind may have simple mathematical analogies, which in turn suggests even more radical reappraisals of the extent to which mathematical concepts can be taken in by young children.

He next considers briefly the ideas of the Bourbaki school in France, in particular the texts of L. Felix and G. Papi, However,

> With all the interest such experiments may have, it is proper to point out that they have not yet given a convincing answer to the problem, either in the sense of the choice of material for school courses nor in the sense of 'mixing' 'classical and contemporary' mathematics. Most often, the general ideas and concepts are put forward side by side with the traditional themes, without being worked out consistently. An example of such a book is the American text 'Modern Mathematics. Algebra Two and Trigonometry' by Rosskopf, Willoughby and Vogeli, where, although some information is given concerning groups, fields and relations, the treatment of complex numbers, elementary transcendental functions (including the trigonometric functions), and vectors follows quite traditional lines without taking up the advantages that could follow from using the general concepts discussed in the other chapters.
>
> A more successful attempt to solve the problem of combining the 'old' and 'new' material in a unified course is contained in G. Papi's book 'La Mathématique Moderne' Vol. 1, 1963. But this book covers only the syllabus of a class following immediately beyond the elementary classes (class VI) and it remains unclear as

[1]Matematika v Shkole 6 (1964) p. 4–8. A full translation of this article was prepared (independently) by H. F. Cleaves, and appeared in the journal 'Mathematics Teaching' 33 pp. 58–62.

to whether the author will be able to overcome the serious difficulties involved in trying to construct the school course as a whole.

Turning to a more detailed consideration of the Bourbaki programme, he allows that a well-illustrated school course based on the ideas of set, relation (in particular the concepts of function, geometrical transformation, equivalence and order), algebraic operations, proximity and space, could be within the grasp of a schoolchild, and could provide rich material for his cultural and mental development. However,

> For us, the cardinal question is the following: if the general ideas and concepts take up the central place in the school mathematics course, and the traditional material, characterized by more particular and concrete qualities, is considered by way of examples and illustrations clarifying the general concepts, shall we not thereby upset the conditions in which, up to now, the pupils have acquired the techniques and knowledge needed in many types of mankind's activities, in the study of the natural sciences and technology, and lastly in the further development of mathematics itself?
>
> To see more clearly what is involved, let us list briefly the 'traditional' themes encountered almost unchanged in the syllabuses of all countries: the number system, starting from the natural numbers and concluding with complex numbers; coordinates and graphs; linear and quadratic equations; elementary functions; the simplest geometrical figures and metrical relations in the triangle and circle; motion; symmetry and homothetical figures; lengths, areas, volumes, and areas of surfaces (traditionally, the circular cylinder, sphere and cone are considered in addition to polygons and the simplest polyhedra). It will be readily agreed that in all changes of the school programme, this material must be retained in some form or other. Consequently, the question resolves itself not into whether or not the listed material should be included in the school course, but, we repeat, into whether or not this material is considered as the basic material to be studied, or as a selection of examples and illustrations to the basic content of the course, which has the aim of acquainting the pupils with the fundamental structures.

Professor Markushevich then refers briefly to the American 'Nine-point Programme,'[1] which he criticises for its failure to include the elements of infinitesimal analysis—a step back, in his view, from Klein's standpoint—and to treat the earlier classes. The resolutions of the Budapest conference organized by UNESCO in 1962 are also discussed (and were described in more detail in an earlier article) but lead only to his agreement with their conclusion that any firm recommendations must be based on a wide range of experimental work, extending over a period of many years.

His final paragraph, which we shall quote in full, concerns developments in the Soviet Union.

> In the USSR, alongside experimental work, work is being carried out on the realization of projects for new syllabuses in the mass school in the very near future. In particular, one such project is being undertaken by the Academy of Pedagogical

[1]Report of the Commission on the Mathematics Program for College Preparatory Mathematics, College Entrance Examination Board, New York, 1959.

Sciences of the RSFSR. This project is not yet completed. However, some of its basic premises can be set out here.

First of all it is necessary to emphasize the philosophical aspect. Mathematics for us is not a simple collection of equal-valued games with more or less complex but in general arbitrary rules, but the science of those most general relations of the real world that can be characterized without reference to the concrete nature of objects ('quantitative' relations in the philosophical sense of the word). As this has a subject-matter irrespective of our wishes, so the choice of material for teaching in the schools cannot be arbitrary, any more than it can be arbitrary in, say, physics or chemistry.

In the school course, the simplest mathematical knowledge, and at the same time that which is most essential for understanding and changing the world, must be laid out in a definite system and sequence. That is why the study of the fundamental number systems (and above all, the systems of whole, rational, and real numbers), linear and quadratic equations, coordinates and graphs, vectors, symmetry, similitude and homothety, the elementary functions, and the fundamentals of differential and integral calculus and their most important applications to geometrical and physical problems—why all this must make up the basic contents of the full school course.

Concepts of a generalizing or unifying character, such, for example, as relation, group, field, linear space, may appear in the course not as basic aspects but as the summary of information brought together by the accumulation of facts and laws providing the grounds for the generalization. Evidently an exception can be made for the concept of a set, since a child already has sufficient experience to enable him to pose and answer questions concerning inclusion or exclusion and the operations on sets.

It is proposed to reduce the introductory period of mathematical education to a minimum length, limiting it to three years (from 7 to 10). Then, over a period of five years, the basic mathematics course must be developed; it will be compulsory for all pupils and will include the final stages of arithmetic, up to the use of algebraic notation and the simplest linear equations, an introductory algebra course (rational operations, extraction of quadratic and cubic roots by means of tables, coordinates and graphs, equations of the first and second degree, the idea of a logarithm and the use of logarithmic slide-rule in calculations), geometry and the elements of trigonometry (triangles, polygons and vectors, similarity and homothety, trigonometrical functions and metric relations in a triangle, relative positions of lines and planes, the most important facts concerning areas and volumes of figures).

Finally, in the upper classes in the different types of schools taking over from the eight-year schools, a course must be brought into being that permits of certain variations in content and character, but which in essential content is devoted to the study of elementary functions (including the circular functions), vectors and motion, derivative and integral and their most important applications, and, if time permits, complex numbers. It is just at this level of education that the structure of mathematical theory itself can be most quickly elucidated. A wider and deeper mathematics course will be provided in the two-year specialized schools for physics and mathematics organized by the universities and scientific research institutes, where a significant amount of extra time is allotted to mathematics, and the selection of students is made on the basis of competitive examinations. In all this work much attention will be given to the splendid experience gained in the schools for computer-programmers, already at work for several years.

From what has been said it follows that a revision of the mathematics teaching must be preceded by rather wide and systematic experimental work in schools of different types and at different stages of education, the results of which must then be discussed and evaluated. This work must lead not only to the basic recommendations concerning the contents of the syllabuses, but also to new text-books and detailed methodological instructions concerning the teaching of different themes of the course. Such work will require many years.

From these remarks it seems probable that, having inherited a down-to-earth and somewhat old-fashioned programme from the pre-revolutionary schools, the Soviet schools will not be in a hurry to change it for a more abstract approach, chiefly in view of their heavy emphasis on the demands of technical education. The calculus seems at last due to make its appearance in the school programme but otherwise, although experiments of their western colleagues are sure to be followed with great interest, the Russians seem likely to proceed very cautiously with their own innovations, basing them on extended and carefully checked experiments.

This is by no means to say that they are inactive in the field of syllabus discussion, and indeed quite the contrary appears to be the case. Professor Gnedenko, in his lectures on Soviet mathematical education to audiences in Australia and New Zealand, described two commissions on mathematics syllabus reform that were then sitting in Moscow, as well as numerous individual experiments. The first of these commissions was organized by the Academy of Sciences of the USSR and was headed by Professor A. N. Kolmogorov. It had as its terms of reference the study of mathematical education at all levels, from the primary schools through the secondary, upper secondary, technical and specialized schools to the universities, engineering institutes, teachers' colleges, and centres of advanced research. The second, also headed by Professor Kolmogorov, had as its more particular aim to survey and recommend changes in the school mathematics syllabuses. One should also mention the all-embracing commission headed by Professor Markushevich (the one he refers to in the final paragraph of the article quoted earlier) which was charged with revising and coordinating syllabuses in all subjects and at all levels of the school programme.

It is not possible to see the question of syllabus reform in the Soviet Union in its proper perspective without taking into account one further factor—the recently introduced secondary schools with specialized education. In many respects this must rank as one of the most important moves in Soviet education since the war. It marks an open break with the stubbornly defended principle that Soviet schoolchildren should receive a common secondary school education. To some extent, of course, this break was implicit in the 1958 reforms with their choice of general or technical education after the eight-year schools, but at that stage the decision could still be considered a matter for the children's own choice. Some at least of the new schools will have competitive entrance examinations, and with this, selection becomes an openly admitted fact. The specialized schools give the Soviet school system a new flexibility, and open up wide possibilities of future development, along lines which have not been considered in quite the same way elsewhere. The provision of a wide variety of specialized secondary schools starting at the 15-year-old level may prove a very appropriate way of tackling the difficulties of upper school education in the twentieth century. At the very least these schools provide Soviet educators with an excellent opportunity for trying out radical experiments in curricular reform and other aspects of upper school teaching.

The possibility of creating specialized schools has been mooted at several times in the history of Soviet education. Some brief suggestions along these lines were given in Khinchin's article as long ago as 1939. The discussions reached a critical stage just before the 1958 reforms, when a remarkable newspaper discussion was carried on in the pages of Pravda and other journals, and many prominent figures gave their views pro and con.[1] Khrushchev's first recommendations included provisions for some experimental schools of this type. However, in the event, it seems that the supporters of the specialized schools were swamped by more conservative elements of the 'polytechnic' campaign and there is no mention of specialized schools in the final decree. But their struggle was not entirely fruitless, because it appears that at the same time or shortly afterwards they won permission to set up the first of what were to be a new type of semi-professional school—the special schools for computer-programmers. By adroitly playing on the current interest in computers and automation, and by insisting that for students of this new profession 'production training' had to be interpreted in terms of practical work on computers and further lecture courses on topics such as numerical approximation and linear programming, the organizers of these schools were able to give their pupils a greatly extended course in higher mathematics as well as specialized courses in numerical methods and programming.

According to Professor Gnedenko, some two hundred or more of these schools have now come into existence, and he has furnished the syllabus details quoted below and in Table 3. These syllabuses are not completely up-to-date, since the reduction to two years upper secondary education has cut back their programme rather severely (they do not get the compensation of time saved from production training, which has allowed the general secondary schools to retain their syllabus essentially unchanged). However, according to the new syllabuses published in 'Matematika v Shkole',[2] the basic mathematics course in the schools for computer programmers is only slightly shortened, the

[1]See the discussion on p. 374 et seq. of 'The Changing Soviet School'.
[2]Matematika v Shkole No. 6 (1964) pp. 45–46.

TABLE 3

CURRICULUM IN GRADES 9–11 OF SOVIET 11-YEAR SCHOOLS
WITH EMPHASIS ON COMPUTER-PROGRAMMING

Subject	Class			Total Number of hours
	9	10	11	
1. Literature	3	3	3	339
2. Mathematics	8	7/6	4	703
3. History and elements of political science	3	3	4/6	410
4. Economic geography	2	2/0	–	112
5. Physics	6	4	3	495
6. Astronomy	–	–	2/0	34
7. Biology	–	2	–	78
8. Chemistry	2	2	3	261
9. Drafting	2	–	–	78
10. Foreign language	3	3	3	339
11. Sport	2	2	2	226
12. Electromechanics and radiotechnology	–	2/4	2/0	156
13. Theory of approximate calculations	3	4/0	–	185
14. Mathematical machines and programming	–	0/4	3	193
15. Practical work with computers	2	2/3	7/9	459
16. Optional subjects	2	2	2	226
			Grand total	4294

main reductions coming in the amount of practical work with computers (reduced to a total of 242 hours) and in side subjects such as the foreign language, literature, and social studies.

Mathematics Syllabus in the Special Schools for Computer Programmers

Form 9

(i) *Basic Mathematics Course* (8 hours/week)
Numerical sequences, limits. Exponential and logarithmic functions, logarithms. General concept of a function of one or two variables. Inequalities of 1st and 2nd degree. Differential coefficient and applications to extreme values of functions. Application of differential coefficient in numerical approximations.

(ii) *Special Course in Numerical Analysis* (3 hours/week plus practical work 2 hours)
Concept of errors of computation. Elements of linear algebra: idea of matrix; multiplication and addition of matrices, unit matrix, inverse matrix. Linear dependence of vectors. Methods of approximate solution of systems of linear equations: Gauss' method, iteration method, Zeidel's method. Interpolation formulae of Lagrange, Stirling, Newton, Bessel. Application of interpolation formulae to construction of tables. The logarithmic scale. Graphical methods; nomograms.

Form 10

(i) *Basic Mathematics Course* (6–7 hours/week)
Right polygons; length and area of circle. Elements of coordinate geometry; equations of straight line, conditions for lines to be parallel or perpendicular, point of intersection of lines. Circle, ellipse, hyperbola and parabola. Vectors. Trigonometric functions of an arbitrary angle; addition formulae.

(ii) *Special Course in Numerical Analysis* (half-year course, 4 hours/week plus practical work 2 hours)
Numerical solution of algebraic and transcendental equations; Horner's method, method of chord and tangent. Numerical integration. Estimation of errors. Numerical solution of differential equations by methods of Euler, Runge-Kutta, Sturm-Adams.

(iii) *Special Course on Mathematical Machines and Machine Programming* (half-year course, 3 hours/week plus practical work 4 hours/week)
Discrete and continuous action machines. 'Small' digital machines. Numerical-analytical machines. Universal electronic computers. Automatic regulation. Component parts of digital computers; schematic structure of machine. Commands. Examples of elementary programmes.
Number systems to different bases: decimal, binary, ternary systems, and systems to bases 4, 8 and 16; transferring from one base to another. Operations in binary system. Errors in representing a number in binary form.
The B.E.C.M.–2 machine: general characteristics; floating decimal notation. Commands, operation code, address. Addition and subtraction, normalization, rounding off, multiplication and division. 'Stop'. Blank for writing commands or numbers. Examples of simple programmes for the B.E.C.M.–2. Punched cards.

Form 11

(i) *Basic Mathematics Course* (4 hours/week)
Complex numbers. Equations of higher degree. Division of polynomials; Bezout's theorem. The fundamental theorem of algebra (without proof). Combina-

torial analysis and elements of probability theory. Solid figures: sphere, cylinder, cone; revision of work on planimeters and solid geometry.

(ii) *Special Course in Mathematical Machines and Machine Programming* (3 hours/week plus practical work 7 hours/week in first half-year, 9 hours/week in second half-year)

Commands for changing control. Readdressing. Simple Cycles. Matrix multiplication. Iteration. Logical Operations. Quantity of information in different memorizing units. Computation of elementary functions. Sub-routines. Block diagram of programme. Control methods. Writing programmes for simple numerical problems.

The creation of these 'schools for computer-programmers' was not the end of the campaign for specialist schools. In 1963 the whole issue was brought up again in a further series of newspaper articles, that seem to have been sparked off by the universities' difficulties in obtaining an adequate supply of mathematically competent schoolchildren to enter their mathematics faculties and so answer the ever-growing demand for mathematics graduates. In an article in Izvestiya in March, 1963,[1] a group of academicians and other scientists from Siberia, headed by the rector of Novosibirsk University, called attention to the revolution in mathematics that had taken place since the development of electronic computers, and compared somewhat critically the Soviet scene with that in the U.S.A. To remedy these deficiencies they suggested setting up specialized schools in the sciences ('Lomonsovskie Uchilishcha) which would take up students for the three years corresponding to the final three years in the secondary schools, exempt them from production training, and give them in its place extensive specialized courses in the selected sciences. Their suggestions were endorsed in a second article by the famous mathematician A. N. Kolmogorov, who went so far as to speak of 'that regrettable pedagogical theory whereby the child must know all subjects equally deeply and as a result knows nothing properly'.[2]

Perhaps as a consequence of the views put forward in this discussion, the universities were permitted to set up some further, more experimental, secondary schools with specialization in mathematics. These schools, of which there are probably some half-dozen at present in existence, differ from the schools for computer-programmers in several respects. They have a purely academic character, and cannot be regarded even formally as a special type of polytechnic school, as are the schools for computer-programmers. They are boarding schools, and select their pupils from a wide area by means of competitive examinations; in

[1]M. Lavrent'ev, S. Sobolev, I. Vekua, D. Shirkov, A. Lyapunov 'The Torch of Talent' Izvestiya, 23rd March, 1963. It is interesting to note that Lavrent'ev (presumably the same one) was one of the principal opponents of the specialized schools in 1958.

[2]A. N. Kolmogorov 'The Search for Talent' Izvestiya, 7th April, 1963.

contrast, the schools for computer-programmers appear to be all day schools and the selection of their students is carried out on the basis of recommendations from local teachers. The new boarding schools must be considered as still an essentially experimental move, whereas the programming schools have already acquired a more or less permanent and official status.

We have not been able to obtain a syllabus for these schools, and indeed it is unlikely that any fixed syllabus yet exists. The Moscow school is notable for the participation of A. N. Kolmogorov, who was reported to have given up all his university activities in order to devote himself to the problems of school-teaching and of creating new syllabuses and teaching methods.

Another special secondary school in 'Akademgorodok', the university town ('science city') not far from Novosibirsk, was visited by a group of American scientists in May 1964, who describe it as follows[1]

'Akademgorodok has a special high school of mathematics, physics and chemistry for advanced students. Young people from schools throughout Siberia are accepted into this school on the basis of competitive examinations. More than 40,000 children, between the ages of 11 and 14 years, are invited to participate in tests which are sent to schools even in the most remote villages. The students who show the greatest ability are brought to larger centres and are given more difficult examinations. Seven hundred children from this group are invited to spend a summer in Akademgorodok, where they are given additional tests and are interviewed by teachers from the advanced high school. During this summer session the children are further evaluated by individual members of the faculty, and 300 students are eventually selected to enter the high school.

Following their graduation from the advanced high school, these students are sought by many universities in the Soviet Union, but most remain in the Science City's graduate training programme.'

The existence of such schools—both the computer-programmer schools and the university schools—creates a number of problems. Not surprisingly, the children from them win most of the olympiad competitions, and take up an undue proportion of the entrance places to the universities. The ordinary schools, which cannot hope to provide corresponding facilities, labour at a consequent disadvantage. No doubt their pupils soon realize that to stay at these schools is only a 'second best', and parents become anxious that their children should have the opportunity of going to one of the special schools. It seems almost inevitable that all the difficulties and opposition attached to selective education, which the Soviet authorities have long sought to avoid, will soon make their appearance. Within the universities, pupils from the special schools continue to cause difficulties because of the large gap between their knowledge, which presumably would allow them to

[1]H. Koprowski et al "A New Science City in Siberia", Science, August 27, 1965, pp. 947-9.

skip at least the first year of university education, and the knowledge of the rest of the students.

Whatever may be the immediate practical difficulties these schools create, their existence places a question mark over the whole future of Soviet education. Whereas ten or fifteen years ago the aim of educational reform might have been expressed in terms of extending the period of universal general education up to ten or eleven years, it is now likely to be in terms of an increasing diversity of specialized upper secondary schools, providing courses not only in technical fields but in the sciences and perhaps the humanities as well. Any proposals for syllabus reform in the Soviet schools, at least in their upper classes, will have to take some stock of this increasing diversification.

*　　*　　*

We now turn to the second question taken up in Khinchin's 1939 article, the training of mathematics teachers. It is hardly surprising that the shortage of teachers should have been a recurring theme of Soviet education, and looking more closely at the problem one is amazed rather that enough teachers could ever have been found to keep the schools open. After the Revolution many suitably qualified teachers were either killed in the civil wars or left the country as emigres. During the 1930's the forced expansion of Soviet education created further shortages; in particular, the opening of many new engineering and technical institutes called away from the schools even those few highly qualified teachers who remained. The Second World War saw a further decimation of the teaching staff, and since that time there has been a continued further increase in the number of schools, now with particular emphasis on technical schools.

The answer to this apparent paradox is probably to be found in the popular enthusiasm for education, the high status of teachers in the Soviet Union, and the widespread acceptance of Lenin's view that the teacher is not only a person to be respected in his own right but a vital component in the development of communism (and of the Soviet Union in particular). Such considerations may have helped to maintain an adequate flow of new personnel into the teaching profession even at times of great shortage. The high status of teachers does not entirely depend upon salary, for they occupy at best a middle range in the Soviet salary spectrum—higher than unskilled workers, but lower than engineers or university staff. In 1961, while I was in Moscow, teachers' salaries seemed to be in the range 70–150 roubles a month, with the director of a school earning perhaps 200 roubles a month or more.[1] This might compare with 50–70 roubles a month for unskilled workers,

[1]The latter figure is quoted by Bereday et al, p. 306.

and 200–300 roubles a month for a university dozent. Secondary school teachers have the possibility of augmenting their basic salaries by taking on special classes or responsibilities, organizing school circles, working overtime, and marking examination papers.[1] Salaries throughout the teaching profession were raised in 1963.

These figures suggest that in fact there may be some discrepancy between the carefully fostered image of the school-teacher and his real-life position. Nevertheless, it is hardly possible to doubt the high value placed on education in the Soviet Union, and to some extent the teacher's status must reflect this situation.

The training of teachers is largely in the hands of various types of teachers' colleges and pedagogical institutes. The primary school teachers (who in general will not be specialists, but will take their class for all subjects) receive their training in teachers' colleges (pedagogicheskie uchilishchie) which at present are classified among the semi-professional schools and provide either a four-year course for students finishing the eight-year schools, or a two-year course for students who have already completed their general secondary education. The secondary school teachers may be trained either in the universities or in special pedagogical institutes. Since the War, the length and quality of the courses given in the pedagogical institutes has improved, and they now provide a five-year training at a comparable level to the universities. The improvement in the pedagogical institutes has, however, been somewhat offset as far as the secondary schools are concerned by the smaller proportion of university graduates entering the teaching profession. This particularly concerns the sciences and mathematics, as we shall see later.

The courses for future mathematics teachers in the pedagogical institutes are outlined in the syllabus quoted below (Table 4) for which we are also indebted to Professor Gnedenko. A similar syllabus was described by B. R. Vogeli in a recent article in the American Mathematical Monthly[2] and is discussed there in rather more detail than we can give to it here. It will be seen that the programme consists of a combination of courses in higher mathematics, covering a wide range of material but probably not in great detail, and a thorough treatment of general professional material. There are long courses devoted to the school programme in mathematics and the techniques for teaching it, and this probably reflects the bias of the programme as a whole.

The work of the pedagogical institutes has often come in for criticism. The level of their courses has been compared unfavourably with university courses, and dire conclusions drawn as to the future of the

[1]Ibid.
[2]'Professional content in Soviet teacher training curricula in mathematics' Am. Math. Monthly 69 (1962) pp. 156–62.

TABLE 4

PROGRAMME FOR SECONDARY SCHOOL MATHEMATICS
TEACHERS IN THE PEDAGOGICAL INSTITUTES

Subject	1	2	3	4	5	6	7	8	9	10	Total
History of the CPSU*	60	80	60	60	–	–	–	–	–	–	260
Political economics*	–	–	–	–	80	60	40	–	–	–	180
Dialectical and historical materialism*	–	–	–	–	–	–	80	40	–	–	120
Foreign Language*	80	80	80	80	–	–	–	–	–	–	320
Psychology	45	45	–	–	–	–	–	–	–	–	90
Pedagogy	–	–	50	50	–	–	–	–	–	–	100
History of Pedagogy	–	–	–	–	72	–	–	–	–	–	72
School Mathematics	40	45	45	45	45	45	45	45	45	–	400
Methods of Mathematics Teaching	–	–	–	–	–	85	85	–	–	–	170
School Hygiene	–	–	–	36	–	–	–	–	–	–	36
Physics	–	85	85	85	85	–	–	–	–	–	340
Astronomy	–	–	–	–	–	–	–	72	–	–	72
Mathematical Analysis	110	110	110	110	–	–	–	–	–	–	440
Algebra	70	70	70	–	–	–	–	–	–	–	210
Foundations of a real variable	–	–	–	–	–	–	56	–	–	–	56
Foundations of a complex variable	–	–	–	–	–	–	–	72	–	–	72
Differential Eqns of Physics	–	–	–	–	–	–	–	–	70	–	70
Number Theory	–	–	–	–	56	–	–	–	–	–	56
Foundations of Mathematics	–	–	–	–	–	60	–	–	–	–	60
Probability	–	–	–	–	–	–	–	56	–	–	56
Analytic Geometry	85	85	–	–	–	–	–	–	–	–	170
Differential Geometry	–	–	–	–	56	–	–	–	–	–	56
Projective Geometry	–	–	–	–	50	50	–	–	–	–	100
Foundations of Geometry	–	–	–	–	–	–	–	–	72	–	72
History of Mathematics	–	–	–	–	–	–	54	–	–	–	54
Computers (theory and practice)	–	–	–	–	–	–	20	–	30	–	50
Mathematical Logic	–	–	–	–	–	–	–	50	–	–	50
Linear Programming	–	–	–	–	–	–	–	60	–	–	60
Optional Courses	–	–	50	50	50	50	100	100	200	–	600
Teaching in Schools	–	–	–	–	–	(3 wks)	(3 wks)	–	–	(Full term)	

The figures in each column represent the total number of hours (including lectures, seminars and supervised exercises) allotted to each subject in the given semester. The figures marked with an asterisk were not given in Professor Gnedenko's table but have been taken from the values quoted for the universities. The figures for linear programming and the optional courses were given in total only and have been incorporated into the table by 'intelligent guesswork'. The periods for teaching practice were also not given explicitly, although the semesters (6, 7 and 10) were indicated. In places where only the total number of hours and the semesters were indicated (e.g. school mathematics 400 hours terms 1–9) we have divided the total among these semesters. Periods for physical education (2 hours/week according to the university programme) are presumably allotted, but were not mentioned in the table.

teaching profession. One result of such criticisms was an increase in the length of their courses from four to five years after the war, and all-round an improvement in quality. Criticisms continue, however. The 'division of labour' between the pedagogical institutes and the universities remains a bone of contention for Soviet educationalists. At present, judging from my own experience five years back, it would seem that very few if any university graduates pass into the secondary schools in subjects such as physics or mathematics,[1] whereas in other subjects, such as languages and literature, the situation is reversed and the majority of graduates enter the secondary schools. Certainly the lack of highly qualified teachers in physics and mathematics is frequently put forward as one of the main reasons for the shortcomings of Soviet secondary school education.

The courses of the pedagogical institutes and teachers' colleges came in for particularly hard-hitting criticism in Khinchin's 1939 article; as his comments would seem to retain much of their force to the present day, we shall quote them in some detail. After the section in his article dealing with the school syllabus, he continues,

> But no matter what the programmes we think up, no matter how good our text-books and teaching manuals, success in the business of school-teaching is determined in the final instance by the quality of our teachers. In this regard matters are unsatisfactory, and with all seriousness it is necessary to underline that the underlying reason for this is the inadequate scientific level of the overwhelming majority of our teaching staff. It is no use demanding of a teacher that he should teach in accordance with the leading ideas of contemporary science if he himself is unfamiliar with such ideas. If we see a teacher in a state of organized helplessness, unable to make his subject clear, attractive and practically relevant, this is almost always a consequence of his scientific immaturity and lack of self-reliance. If, let us say, the order of exposition in some one or two chapters in the standard text-book is different from the order in the syllabus, this is considered with us a catastrophe, an organizational scandal; instructions and methodological documents are prepared at emergency rate, frequently turning out to be unhappy results of the burning hurry; accusations are registered in the names of the syllabus-compilers and text-book authors. And yet any teacher capable not only of following a ready-made crib but of showing even the smallest amount of independent scientific thought will surely be able to cope with such a trivial detail himself, without any methodological assistance from the side.
>
> It is necessary to say straight out that we teach our future teachers a great deal, including much that is unnecessary, but we fail to teach them the most important thing of all for a teacher—the ability to act as scientific organizer and scientifically competent host for the teaching process. In recent times, our press, especially the Uchitel'skaya Gazeta, has given much attention to the education of teachers; in its pages responsible members of the Higher Schools Committee and the Narkompros have put forward a whole series of undoubtedly useful and important measures for setting to rights the matter of teachers' education. But for some reason all these articles completely avoid its main defect.

[1] In one of his lectures Professor Gnedenko referred to 3 of the 400—odd students graduating from the Mathematics and Mechanics Faculty of Moscow University choosing secondary-school teaching as their career.

Take a look at any report of the Higher Schools Committee or the Narkompros dealing with the pedagogical schools, evaluating their work and suggesting measures to improve it. You will see there references to mistakes in the work of the directors, deans and departments, you will see director's instructions to his deans and departments, but you will almost never find references to defects in the students' work, and you will never find instructions addressed to the students. Quite often it is impossible to discern from such a document that in addition to directors, deans and departments, our institutes also contain students.

This is extremely characteristic of the whole style of working of our higher educational institutes. The student is regarded not as a mature and responsible participant, but only as a work-object for whose successes and failures are responsible, in the first place, director, dean, and professor. If the student does not learn well, the blame if you please is sought in the first place in the director's office, in the dean's office, in the professorial rooms: the student, however, plays the role of production material, and of course there is nothing to look for there!

The student himself organizes nothing in the teaching process. From the first day of study up to the last state examination, the director, the dean and the professor think everything out for him. For six hours a day the student sits out lectures or other compulsory work under his teacher's supervision. Then he is supposed to 'work through', i.e. repeat, what he has heard using notes or the indicated text-book. Later, he has to sit examinations, and here too he is excluded from any participation even in the external organization of the business. The measures taken by the institutes' administrations to 'stimulate independent work" are essentially laughable. Instead of stimulating they do everything possible to quench initiative at the source.

When talk is raised of 'independent work' the first things to be mentioned are 'consultations'. More consultations! But what does this mean in practice? In practice, it means that a student who is unable to follow some detail in the lecture or text-book, instead of overcoming his bewilderment by his own efforts, which might sometimes take no more than ten minutes, learns to turn at once to the teacher in order to obtain a ready answer. In practice this means that a student who needs some theorem, instead of searching through two or three text-books in order to find its proof for himself (and we all know how instructive such searches can be) goes to his teacher and obtains a specific instruction: such-and-such book, page such-and-such. And these are called measures to stimulate independence!

Let us suppose that the students organize a scientific circle—a genuinely promising beginning. But in order to 'stimulate independence', the teachers have to make up a list of themes, determine their sequence, indicate all the appropriate literature on the given theme down to the page number, and, yes, more consultations with the students, over the preparation of their talks. In a word, this beginning, in its conception organized and carried out on the students' own initiative, is made to approximate by all possible means to the usual process of passive learning. It is typical that the directors of the institutes, when they wish to hear about the progress of these circles, impute the responsibility not to the students (for example the selection bureau of the circle), but to the heads of departments, evidently considering a scientific circle to be as subordinated and regimentated as all other such beginnings in the teaching world . . .

But they go even further. To help the students in their 'independent work' they sometimes assign them specific teachers, which means in fact quite undisguised coaching. We know of cases where wily students have attempted to get themselves assigned in mass to such coaches, and only the energetic opposition of the scientific staff has prevented the occurence of such an extremely dangerous move.

At the same time, the optional courses and seminars—that is to say, just those things most capable of developing independence—are found in our teaching institutes at the very lowest ebb. It may happen that a professor enthusiastically undertakes to read an optional course, and that the students are eager to hear it, but the director and dean attempt by all open and indirect means to ensure that the course does not take place. At the basis of this strange and at first sight incomprehensible tendency lies always the inappropriate fear that the students may somehow be distracted by enthusiasm for the science itself from their proper occupation—cramming.

As a result of all these and many similar 'measures' a student of one of our teaching colleges is very soon transformed into that familiar creature, wholly, up to the very last state examination, absorbed by the problem of how to swot up the set material from such a page to such a page and disgorge it in the examination. We all know only too well those notorious 'consultations' before the state examinations, when you will never hear a single scientific question but you are literally smothered with insistent demands to state authoritatively about some theorem 'do we have to know it or not?' 'Do we have to know two definitions of the continuity of a function or is it permissible to learn off only one?' Such meetings will turn anyone's hair grey who really cares about the state of the country's education.

What can we expect from a teacher with such an education? How can a man organize the work of a whole class if he has, throughout the period of his four-year course, been carefully and by every means deprived of the possibility of organizing even the smallest detail of his own education? Is it not as if schools training, say, swimming-instructors, up to and including the final examinations refused to allow their pupils to get into the water except on water-wings?

What then must be done in order that all this should turn out differently, that the future teacher should leave the teaching institutes scientifically well-shod and organizationally literate?

For this, it is first of all necessary to move from the system of senseless school-type training to a system of proper scientific education. It is necessary to pay attention to widening the students' scientific outlook, to deepening their understanding of the essential ideas, the main bases of science—not to the formal learning-off of particular, scattered, scientific facts. And finally it is essential to create in our pedagogical institutes and teachers' colleges a genuine scientific atmosphere and to cultivate in the students a love for their science above a striving for examination successes.

The organizational measures that should be taken to achieve these aims are quite clear. They consist firstly in an appreciable reduction in the number of hours given to supervised work and a corresponding transfer of the centre of gravity to genuinely independent work. It is by no means necessary, as it is customary with us to suppose, that every theorem set out in detail in the text-books should be proved in detail by the lecturer. The lectures should neither repeat nor replace the text-books, but should give the basic context for and illuminate the main ideas of the material that the student will study for himself in the text-book. If we take up this point of view, then the number of lectures in the majority of subjects can be cut down by a half, and from this the teaching standard will only improve.

It is also essential to stop all the petty watching over the student's every step, to start looking on the student as a grown-up and fully responsible worker, for whose progress he is in the first instance responsible himself. It is essential to accustom him to the thought that the department and faculty can at best offer him assistance, and that it is he himself who is the organizer of his time and work. He must be able to find for himself the necessary literature, and, before coming for consultations, he must make every effort to try and master his difficulties on his own. It is essential to cut out at the root all attempts to organize 'coaching'. It is essential to completely outgrow all appearances of 'liberalism' in marking the student's work and, in so doing, to take into account that such 'liberalism' has many faces and is very resourceful. Putting down too high marks is by no means its only appearance. When the directors or the dean require a professor to re-examine a student four times in the course of a single term, on the same subject, finally wearing him down to the point that, in desperation, he gives the student the mark 'adequate', then this is an even worse appearance of 'liberalism', for it is caused by that same dangerous fault—well-known under the name 'percentomania'.

It is essential, finally, that the programme of optional courses in our pedagogical institutes should be widely extended, together with seminars and students' circles working on the basis of the students' own initiative. It would not do to limit ourselves in this direction to mere wishes with no obligation attached; it is necessary to work out on the basis of each institute's staff its requirements in the way of optional courses and seminars.

These then are the basic steps towards improving the teaching regime in our pedagogical institutes; their necessity should be evident to all.

Judging from the programmes described earlier, it would seem that, at least in the matter of providing the student-teachers with good mathematical material, including optional courses, the pedagogical institutes have made considerable progress since the time of Khinchin's remarks. Indeed, Vogeli compares their courses quite favourably with courses in the United States for future mathematics teachers. On the other hand it would seem very probable that his other criticisms, regarding the regimentation of the student's work and his lack of independence, apply with just as much force at the present time. Going back to my own experience of Soviet universities, the students are kept down to a very rigid timetable, with 'periods' marked off for each subject, and in general are treated much more like children than they would be, say, in Oxford and Cambridge. In fact it would be hard to imagine two systems of university education which differed so completely in their psychological treatment of the students. And although the able students will soon reach a fairly comparable level, the effects of such differences on the students of lower ability, who often need particular encouragement to develop their own initiative, is likely to be more pronounced. It is probable that the pedagogical institutes still have a real weakness from this point of view.

Let us turn now to the comments of a more recent critic, Academician I. Vekua, until recently rector of Novosibirsk University. His article, entitled 'School, Teacher, and Life', appeared in Pravda in 20th July, 1964. After describing some of the difficulties faced by the universities at the time of their entrance examinations, when they are forced to reject many students because of their inadequate understanding of trigonometry, complex numbers, and other parts of the mathematics syllabus (as well as for failings in other subjects), he comments,

> These shortcomings are usually put down to deficiencies in the school courses, syllabuses and text-books. Continuous detailed work is undertaken to improve them, but each time, even in their revised form, they give rise to much the same criticisms. What then is wrong, why is it that the workers in national education, the scholars and pedagogues, are unable to find a way out of this situation?
>
> One feels that the main reason for these vexing failures and miscalculations on the part of the syllabus-compilers and text-book writers lies in the desire to give the schoolchildren as much information as possible from very varied fields of science. The secondary schools (it is said) should turn out pupils with an all-round development. And thus the number of subjects studied grows, the text-books swell, and the older schoolchildren are required to work, in the classroom and at home, up to ten or twelve hours per day. It is not surprising that even the most industrious and gifted of the schoolchildren cannot always thoroughly master all that is studied.

From these grounds he draws two main conclusions: firstly that the time has come to undertake a thorough revision of the school courses with a view to throwing out material that is not essential or has lost its relevance in the present day. His suggestions here repeat some of the ideas we have already touched upon in connection with syllabus reform and the development of the specialized secondary schools. The second factor is the teacher himself.

> Not in vain is it said, as the teacher, so the pupil. With outstanding teachers, children master their knowledge creatively and think boldly. But unhappily there are also teachers whose pupils can only mumble a rigmarole that they have never properly understood.
>
> Of course, it happens that some people enter the teaching profession without having the necessary knowledge for it. From such 'teachers' nothing can be expected. But how many examples is it possible to bring up of teachers who are conscientious and experienced, but who do not have time or simply for various reasons are unable to keep up with the most recent developments in their science, and who from year to year lag further behind its present level? Of course, in such cases the teacher must be helped. However, much here depends on his initial training, the knowledge that he acquired while he was still a student. In general, one is lead to the conclusion that among teachers, especially the younger ones, there are not many specialists with really high qualifications. In my opinion, this is what constitutes 'the root of the evil', and is the chief cause of the short-comings in the work of the secondary schools.
>
> It is well-known that our teachers are trained in the pedagogical institutes. In passing it may be noted that many of these institutes lack highly qualified teaching staff, and are inadequately provided with modern equipment for teaching and research work. Some grounds for alarm are also caused by the state of pedagogical science, as unfolded before the future teachers. Students study it from long out-dated text-books, and to some extent in a purely formal manner. It is under-standable that under such circumstances many graduates of the pedagogical institutes do not measure up to the high requirements that we have the right to demand from the people's teachers.
>
> Here it would not be out of place to recall the past, when the sources of pedagogical thought, and the centres for training highly qualified secondary school teachers, were acknowledged to be the universities. At the present time, however, these have unfortunately been pushed to the edge of the scene. It is now

very seldom that one meets people with a university education among the secondary school teachers of mathematics, physics, and chemistry. Can this really be normal?

The breadth, 'universality', of his theoretical training, his mastery of the technique of independent scientific research, make the teacher with a university badge on his breast an absolutely essential figure in the secondary school. I am not asserting that the universities should provide all the teaching staff. That would be unrealistic, an utopian fantasy. But let there be just two or three university graduates in every school, bringing with them the love of scientific research. Together with the older, more experienced teachers there is no doubt that they could exert an influence on the whole collective, helping to build up a creative atmosphere in the school, to raise the culture of the children's teaching, and bringing to the pupils an inextinguishable thirst for knowledge.

Indeed, the very tendency of growth of pedagogical science is for it to seek persistently for links with the universities, with sciences such as sociology, cybernetics, and others. All this indicates that there is an urgent necessity to considerably extend the training of teachers in the universities. Why should the universities not be oriented towards, say, the training of teachers for the upper classes, while the eight-year schools draw their teachers from the pedagogical institutes?

It would seem appropriate to link the pedagogical institutes closely with the universities, and in some places even to reorganize them in the shape of pedagogical faculties of the universities themselves. In any case, the network of pedagogical institutes should be re-examined, and the training of future teachers concentrated where there are a sufficient number of teachers with high qualifications—professors and dozents, doctors and candidates of science—and also a good material-technical basis. To this end it is also necessary to strengthen the ties between the pedagogical institutes and industry, construction organizations, kolkhozes and sovkhozes, as well as institutes training engineering personnel. This would have a good effect on the training of teachers, on the establishment of polytechnic schools, and on the training of their graduates for production work.

It is quite incomprehensible why in some regions or districts there are two or even three pedagogical institutes, literally only some tens of kilometers away from each other, all equally badly provided with both staff and equipment.

In our view, the teacher with a university diploma should be given certain advantages. Such a move would help to attract talented young people to the teaching profession, and to create the prerequisites necessary for a free interchange of staff between scientific institutions and the higher educational institutes and schools and vice versa.

If we attempt to solve the problem of training the teacher with full seriousness and a proper resolution, then there is no doubt that even within the next few years it would be possible to make a significant improvement in children's education, in bringing it closer to life, and in training in better time worthy replacements for the builders of communism.

Finally, I would like to quote a few paragraphs from Professor Gnedenko's article 'On the training of a mathematics teacher'[1] that appeared in Matematika v Shkole together with Professor Markushevich's article quoted earlier. Gnedenko is concerned here with the ever increasing role of mathematics in modern life, and some general desiderata for the mathematics teacher and his training that follow from these changes.

[1] Matematika v Shkole 1964, No. 6, pp. 8–20,

The education and formation of the future mathematics teacher cannot be considered a satisfactory process; it requires serious and all-round discussion. From the mathematics teacher is required not only a good knowledge of his subject but also the ability to arouse his students' interest in it. This is a great and wonderful ability, and one that it is essential to foster among the graduates of the teaching colleges. We know many teachers who can hold the attention of most of the pupils in their class and who make their subject so interesting that many of their pupils dream of becoming mathematicians, and in fact do so. Many times in the university I have chanced to meet with several graduates from the same class, who have been brought up with a love of, and enthusiasm for, mathematics. And by the side of their love for mathematics they preserved a genuine gratitude to their school-teacher, who had sown in them this love and been able to nurture it over a period of many years. Unfortunately, there is an even greater number of teachers who are not only unable to awaken a love for mathematics, but who cannot even awaken an interest in it, or in scientific knowledge. If teachers of the first type achieve their successes by many routes, the means by which interest and ability are killed are more or less identical—lack of interest on the part of the teacher himself both towards science and towards teaching, and also his own poor scientific training. How can we achieve the situation where the majority of mathematics teachers are masters of their trade, and their work brings joy both to their pupils and to themselves?

In answering this question, we insist in the first place on the necessity of defining what should be taught to the future mathematics teacher. In the Soviet Union there are still two rather widely separated points of view. The first supposes that the teacher should first of all be armed with a knowledge of general pedagogical theory, the principles of psychology, didactics, and particular methods. The large number of pedagogical subjects in the mathematics and physics faculties of the pedagogical institutes is without doubt a result of what is to some extent the 'victory' of this point of view. The other sees as the foundation of the training of a teacher a good training in mathematics itself. The mathematics-physics and mathematics-mechanics faculties of the universities, which still send a certain proportion of their graduates to the secondary schools, embody just this point of view. On several occasions I have heard educational workers say that for the first two or three years the university-trained graduates compare unfavourably with the graduates of the pedagogical institutes, but that later they achieve better results. This observation is of such basic importance that a systematic investigation should be carried out, and a choice made on the basis of factual evidence.

I myself consider that although the future teacher cannot do without the fundamentals of a general methodological and pedagogical training, still less can a good mathematics teacher do without a wide training in contemporary mathematics. How can it be possible to teach a subject well, if one does not have a deep understanding of it oneself, if one has not mastered it freely but knows only pieces here and there? The authority of the teacher will be hopelessly undermined when the children discover that his knowledge differs but little from that which they have to master themselves. And here neither a knowledge of methodology, nor a knowledge of pedagogy, nor attractive personal characteristics will help.

Yet the mathematical education of the future teacher must not be constructed to the same plan as that of the future mathematics research worker. If in the second case, besides a wide mathematical education, a deep penetration into some relatively narrow part of mathematics is needed, then from the mathematics teacher something rather different is required. First of all, he must be able to visualize the structure of contemporary mathematics as a whole. Further, he must be well aware of its links with other sciences and its practical applications. He must be well acquainted with the history of mathematics and of mathematical discoveries. He must picture to himself the psychology of mathematical discoveries, the process which leads to such discoveries. This requirement places certain demands not only on the character of the courses on the history of mathematics, but perhaps also on that of other courses that he must attend. He must have a store of interesting problems and must master the art of solving complicated problems and examples. He must be convinced of the importance of his work himself, and have the gift of convincing others. Often he will encounter pupils or their parents who consider that for some given person mathematical knowledge will not be necessary, since he or she is going to be a doctor, an economist, a painter or a writer. At the present time, of course, when a doctor approaches a patient's bedside he determines his illness not by computation but by a careful examination and a comparison with the known symptoms of the disease. But, first, does it follow from this that the future doctor will have no need of mathematics or of that specific mode of thinking that is peculiar to mathematics? And secondly, will it always be like this, and will mathematics never come to the aid of medicine? I know that it will. But this must be known to every teacher of mathematics, and he must be able to talk about it so as to carry conviction. Although it may happen that the given student may, in the course of his life, never find himself in need of mathematics, yet that style of thinking which it teaches is certain to be useful to him.

The teacher must be able to awaken an interest in mathematics even with the limited material that the schoolchildren have to cover. In order to do this, he himself must clearly see that mathematics is not an ossified science, formulated in the times of Euclid, or, at best, of Newton and Leibniz, but a science that is ever young, that has a multitude of unsolved problems in front of it, and immense possibilities of growth. He must be able to make links that join the school course with burning issues of the day, to show how old formulations of problems or even old methods of solution can be given fresh light and made to sparkle in new colours. It will be clear to anyone that this cannot be achieved unless the teacher himself has reached a very high level of mathematical and general culture.

In connection with society's continual demands for ever greater numbers of people with the inclination towards and habit of scientific thinking, there arises the importance of educating teachers in such a way that they are not only capable of expounding the school course in a literate and methodical fashion, but also of awakening schoolchildren's interest in science, and communicating to them the joy of discovery and the splendour of the scientific achievements that the rising generation is destined to bring into being. Elegant problems, demanding an unorthodox approach; independent creative work in establishing proofs; the discovery of errors in plausible but erroneous arguments—all these are elements of creative work that are capable of giving immense satisfaction to the schoolchild, and of providing an incomparable stimulus to further study.

The teacher not only passes on to his pupils the course material, but he leads them forward into life, and his task is to ensure that his pupils learn to see further and deeper than their predecessors. His activities must result in the pupils being able to visualize for themselves, with reasonable clarity, the bright image so well expressed in the words of Newton, 'If I have seen further than most, it is because I stood on the shoulders of giants.' Contemporary youth has a greater number of such gargantuan ancestors; therefore it has further and harder to go to reach the shoulders of our contemporary scientific giants. And if this is true, then to lose time is fatal, and the school must help the schoolchild not only to traverse the path to the foot of the peaks, but also to cultivate the habit of hard work, of persistent independent effort, and the ability to reach solutions through their own efforts, without the help of hints obtained from consultations.

In order to teach well it is necessary to have the initiative in one's own hands, and, consequently, a certain amount of freedom in conducting the lesson. It is sometimes more useful to spend an hour in discussing with the schoolchildren questions which have no immediate relation to the set theme, than to limit oneself to an exposition of the course material. A successful discussion, arousing the interest of the participants, is capable of giving incomparably more to school study than is a formal, uninspired lesson. And as the talented actor can plan a certain role dozens of times and in each new performance live anew the events in the life of the hero, so the mathematics teacher, proving some theorem for the hundredth time, must relive the joy of discovery; otherwise it will be hard for the students in their turn to share in this excitement.

This quotation brings us to the end of this survey. It seems a fair conclusion to say that the problems occupying the minds of Soviet writers in the sphere of mathematical education—problems both practical and theoretical, psychological, organizational, methodological —have very close analogues, if not exact counterparts, in the West. Of course, it may be objected that the views we have quoted are exclusively those of university professors and perhaps not representative of the teaching profession itself or of its administration. It should be borne in mind, however, that, at least in a subject such as mathematics, the university professor in the Soviet Union is commonly much more closely involved with the schools and their administration and guidance, than he is here. It would be wrong to think of the writers we have quoted as mere voices crying out in the wilderness. On the other hand, it is probably true their opinions are not the ultimate authority in Soviet education, and they presumably attach more importance to the need for educational reform than would be felt by the community at large, or the politicians. Nevertheless the rapidly changing role of mathematics in the modern world, its visibly growing importance in maintaining and further advancing the achievements of the Soviet Union as of all other major countries, give the Soviet mathematician an unprecedentedly strong position from which to advance his views. Perhaps the Soviet Union is fortunate that among those who moulded these views have been such perceptive, outspoken, and humanitarian thinkers as A. Ya. Khinchin.

Note added on proof, 18/10/67

In the last year, some dramatic changes have taken place on the Soviet educational scene. It is not possible to treat these here in detail, but I would like to summarize the main points insofar as they affect Soviet mathematical education.

The changes were outlined in a resolution of the Communist Party Central Committee and the Council of Ministers of the U.S.S.R., which was published in Izvestiya, 19th November, 1966 under the heading 'On measures to further improve the work of the secondary schools of general education'. Among the most important points were

(1) a general rationalization and streamlining of syllabuses in the

general schools, to bring their courses into better correspondence with the demands of present-day science and technology;

(2) starting from class 7, the introduction of optional courses of a specialized nature, to take up 2 hours per week in classes 7 and 8, and 4 hours per week in classes 9 and 10;

(3) the development of a network of upper secondary schools (both day and boarding) providing specialized education in subjects chosen from both the sciences and the humanities.

The resolution also called for increased expenditure on school buildings and equipment, limitations on the maximum number of students in a class, and more support for the schools from local party organizations, factories, sovkhoz and kolkhoz. Party organizations are called on to ensure that universal secondary education is achieved by 1970. The ministries of education and associated organizations are asked to give priority to the creation of new text-books to cover the new syllabuses.

The changes are to come into operation over the remainder of the present 5-year period, which ends in December 1970.

The first 1967 issue of Matematika v Shkole carried the projected syllabus for the new school course in mathematics. This is the syllabus prepared by the commission on the school mathematics programme described earlier, with Kolmogorov as its chairman. The following issue contained a commentary by Kolmogorov outlining some of the different points of view that had been expressed during the working of the commission, and explaining their final decisions.

The most important innovations are as follows. In the eight-year schools, the basic notions of algebra are to be introduced in classes 4 and 5 (ages 11–13) at the same time as the detailed study of fractions and decimals. In classes 6–8 the discussion of algebraic transformations and equations is limited to the most straightforward and striking material, leaving time to introduce the logarithmic and exponential functions in class 8 (ages 14–15), along with the use of log tables and the logarithmic slide rule; simple differentiation appears in class 9; and in class 10, simple integration and the elements of probability theory.

The geometry course suffers an even more radical revision. Up to class 5, geometry is to be considered largely as an experimental rather than a deductive subject, and when the deductive element is introduced, it is to be based on a wider and more explicit set of propositions assumed without proof than in the traditional Euclidean exposition. Much of the older course, for example, the theorems on metric relations in a circle, is omitted. In the later classes, the emphasis is on the study of transformations (translation, rotation, reflection) and vector methods.

Besides the general course (which will be taken by all students in the general schools) there is some discussion of optional courses in mathematics, starting from class 7. The syllabuses described are in the nature of a supplement to the general course, giving details on topics, such as set theory, some aspects of geometry, complex numbers, which are only touched on in the main course. This optional course is designed to take up only two hours per week in classes 9 and 10, leaving two hours per week free for optional courses in other subjects.

List of General References

1. Korol, A. C. Soviet Education for Science and Technology. New York (Wiley), 1957.
2. Bereday, G. Z. F., Brickman, W. W. and Read, G. H. The Changing Soviet School. London (Constable) 1960.
3. de Witt, N. Education and Professional Employment in the U.S.S.R. Washington (National Science Foundation) 1961.
4. King, E. J. (Ed.). Communist Education. London (Methuen) 1963.
5. Grant, N. Soviet Education. London (Penguin) 1964; (L.U.P.) 1965.
6. Gnedenko, B. V. 'Mathematical Education in the U.S.S.R.' Am. Math. Monthly 64 (1957) pp. 389–408.
7. Gnedenko, B. V. 'Mathematical Education in the U.S.S.R.' Austral. Math. Teacher 21, No. 3 (1965), pp. 45–59.
8. Vere-Jones, D. 'The Mathematician's Tale' Survey No. 52 (1964), pp. 52–60.
9. Korol, A. C. 'Soviet Research and Development: its organization, personnel and funds". Cambridge (Mass.) (M.I.T.) 1965.

A number of volumes from the two Russian series 'Library of the School Mathematical Circle' and 'Popular Lectures in Mathematics' have recently been translated into English or listed as in the process of translation. These include two series, 'Topics in Mathematics', from the Survey of East European Mathematical Literature under the general direction of A. L. Putnam and I. Wirszup (Chicago), and 'Popular Lectures in Mathematics', under the general editorship of I. N. Sneddon, published by Pergamon. The list of titles in these series is as follows:

Popular Lectures in Mathematics

Edited by I. N. Sneddon

Topics in Mathematics
Edited by A. L. Putnam and I. Wirszup

1. Configuration Theorems. B. I. Argunov and L. A. Skorntskov
2. What is Linear Programming? A. S. Barsov
3. Equivalent and Indecomposible Figures. V. G. Boltyanski
4. Mistakes in Geometric Proofs. Ya. S. Dubnov
5. Proofs in Geometry. A. I. Fetisov
6. Induction in Geometry. L. I. Golovina and I. M. Yaglom
7. Computation of Areas of Oriented Figures. A. M. Lopshits
8. Areas and Logarithms. A. I. Markushevich
9. Summation of Infinitely Small Quantities. I. P. Natanson
10. Hyperbolic Functions. V. G. Shervatov
11. How to Construct Graphs, and the Simplest Maxima and Minima Problems
    G. E. Shilov and I. P. Natanson
12. The Method of Mathematical Induction. I. S. Sominskii
13. Algorithms and Automatic Computing Machines. B. A. Trakhtenbrot
14. An Introduction to the Theory of Games. E. S. Ventsel
15. The Fibonacci Numbers. N. M. Vorobyev

Several other volumes are also available, of which we would mention especially
A. M. and I. M. Yaglom: Challenging Mathematical Problems with Elementary Solutions. Volumes 1 and 2 (Holden-Day, San Francisco, 1964)

E. B. Dynkin and V. A. Uspenskii: Mathematical Conversations. Many colour problems. Problems from Number Theory. Random walks. (D. C. Heath, Boston, 1963)

D. O. Shklarsky, N. H. Chentsov and I. M. Yaglom: The U.S.S.R. Problem Book (W. H. Freeman, San Francisco, 1962).